a practicum of group
psychotherapy

a practicum
of group
psychotherapy

Asya L. Kadis · Jack D. Krasner · Charles Winick
POSTGRADUATE CENTER FOR PSYCHOTHERAPY, NEW YORK

S. H. Foulkes, M.D.
GROUP-ANALYTIC SOCIETY, LONDON

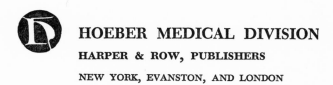

HOEBER MEDICAL DIVISION
HARPER & ROW, PUBLISHERS
NEW YORK, EVANSTON, AND LONDON

SECOND PRINTING OCTOBER, 1965

A PRACTICUM OF GROUP PSYCHOTHERAPY
Copyright © 1963 by Hoeber Medical Division,
Harper & Row, Publishers, Incorporated
Printed in the United States of America

K-P

LIBRARY OF CONGRESS CATALOG CARD NUMBER: 62-19881

contents

preface

THIS volume is a handbook of group psychotherapy in the sense that it is an overview of the significant practical aspects of group psychotherapy. Our efforts have been directed toward setting forth those aspects of this rapidly expanding field that are relevant to persons working in a wide variety of treatment situations and contexts. Theoretical discussion, although limited, is introduced where it has relevance to specific problems of practice.

The exposition includes material of interest to beginning and experienced practitioners of guidance, counseling, as well as psychoanalytic group psychotherapy, although the major direction of the book is based on psychodynamics. The contents of the book are derived to a considerable extent from our experience in training group psychotherapists at the Postgraduate Center for Psychotherapy in New York. Many of the concepts and formulations in this book have resulted from some years of experimentation with different methods of training successive groups of student group psychotherapists at the Center.

Citations to the literature of group psychotherapy are made when they are pertinent to the discussion in the text. The annual reviews of the literature which appear in sources such as *Annual Review of Psychology, International Journal of Group Psychotherapy* and *Yearbook of Psychoanalysis* make it simple for the reader interested in a particular area to follow up additional citations.

The writing of this book has been a truly cooperative effort, with each of the authors participating in the writing of every chapter. We are especially grateful to our distinguished English colleague, Dr. S. H.

Foulkes, not only for his introductory chapter, but also for his penetrating and detailed analysis of and comments on the penultimate version of the manuscript. Dr. Foulkes has provided us and group psychotherapists everywhere an example of knowledge, and perhaps more importantly of wisdom.

A. L. K.
J. D. K.
C. W.

New York

a practicum of group psychotherapy

psychotherapy and group 1
psychotherapy

S. H. Foulkes, M. D.

PATIENTS in a group are the focus of this book. The particular kind of group in which we are interested is concerned with psychotherapy. If you wish to treat a patient by psychotherapy, you must assume that he is expected to change. Here at once a number of questions arise: *who* expects him to change? If only you or someone of his surroundings, *e.g.*, his family, expect him to change, this is obviously not enough. Therefore you must claim that he himself wants to change. If so, why does he want to change? In what respect does he want to change? In what way does he think that the change is to come about? Why does he come to you for this? We well know that all of these questions have a conscious and an unconscious aspect. It is, therefore, of limited value to ask the patient these questions, and you cannot expect to get answers from him that will lead you far.

Rather it is a matter of finding out the answers to all these questions by inference, based on all sorts of communications, responses, and attitudes which the patient presents or betrays. The same is true for his entire attitude toward the proposed treatment procedure and toward you. In judging these too, your own conclusions must be based not merely and, probably, not mainly on what is manifest and con-

1

scious. You will form impressions as to how difficult it is for him to become aware of something previously unperceived, how long a way he may have to go to accept parts of himself which hitherto he had not realized. In this way, among others, you gain some appreciation of his capacity for insight, integration, as well as other factors. You also get a first inkling of the strength and mode of his defenses—that is to say, the strength and way in which he will resist change.

If you have arrived at a fair picture concerning these points and find the situation on the whole quite favorable for change, you have assessed something which is largely comprised in the term "motivation." This is perhaps the most significant factor for indication for psychotherapy and is more important than the diagnosis. If the formal diagnosis is meaningful and not a mere label, it will correspond to the psychopathological dynamics fairly well, at least in a general way.

A conversional hysteric, for instance, might present you with some physical complaint, say being sick and vomiting. This may appear quite unrelated to any situation. If he is confident enough of his defenses, he may be very eager for treatment, he may be free from anxiety, pleasant and cooperative. You would not be surprised if you found that while this patient adhered to a belief in the ultimate physical nature of his disturbance, he came to you readily on the authoritative advice of his physician. He might expect a purely symptomatic cure from you, maybe on a magical basis—and he would readily bestow magical powers on you so long as you maintain this fiction with him. On the other hand, he may pay lip service to psychological causation (preferably in early childhood) which he will expect you to discover and thus cure him.

A patient with a phobia, such as being afraid to go out alone, or travel in a train, perhaps under some specified circumstances, will have a much more frankly psychological approach. His defenses will be expressed correspondingly in different ways and his own theory of treatment will be correspondingly different.

In these simple examples, the psychopathology and the diagnosis correspond and indicate the task and nature of the therapeutic process. Even here, however, the mere diagnostic label would not tell us enough. For instance, the hysteric mentioned might soon show deep hypochondriacal fears or he might or might not relate himself in a more or less central or vital way to the therapist, thus throwing the field wide open for a therapeutic approach; or he might soon find a way of breaking up the treatment situation. Most diagnostic labels, however, are not dynamically significant or they cover too large a ground. It follows from all this that we cannot well express suitability for psychotherapy in terms of diagnoses and still less can we construe a differential indication as to the form of psychotherapy as, for instance, whether better in an individual (two-personal) or in a group situation. Motivation and capacity for change seem more important.

Symptoms and Change

We must, therefore, make a psychodynamic assessment of the problem with which the patient presents us. Such a psychodynamic profile has multidimensional aspects and should include at least a provisional idea of the strength of the various positions (e.g., paranoid) according to the level of regression and corresponding defense. In the light of this, we may have some tentative answers to the questions: Can he change? How far? By what means? What can we do about it? It is important that these questions be answered in the light of the practical situation in which you and the patient find yourselves and that the aims you hope to achieve are consistent with the limitations set by the reality in which you work.

The patient's own conclusions and manifest ideas may correspond fairly well with your conception of his real problem or, on the contrary, they may be poles apart.

Meantime, on our part, we have made a basic assumption. We have assumed or, better perhaps, accepted, that a symptom is a symptom and not the true disturbance which causes the patient to come to us. Furthermore, we have accepted that the disturbance is not a disease in the sense of a process which has descended upon our patient from outside of himself. Rather we have learned from the experience of half a century, an experience confirmed in every single case over again, that this disturbance is brought about by unresolved conflicts often referred to as "problems." From this it follows that our idea of therapy is that the *patient* must change, himself, not something outside himself, and not that something must be changed for him. What the conflicts are and why they are not resolved and why, for all the suffering, change is so desperately resisted, cannot be gone into here. For this, I would have to recall the whole psychoanalytic body of observation.

Our concept of the nature of the change which is desired differs, therefore, fundamentally from the patient's concept. If it did not differ, he would not need to consult us. We can confidently say that if, as a result of our treatment, the patient comes around, by genuine conviction based on his own experience, from his original idea as to what is wrong with him, and how it could be cured, to our idea as just formulated, he must be on the way to recovery. The first essential and general aim of all psychotherapy is thus clear. I like to refer to it as *the move from the symptom to the problem*. This is major progress in psychotherapy though only part of the process.

The individual steps which bring about such change could also be called "learning," but this term could easily be misleading. Learning suggests an intellectual process and this is not at all what is wanted primarily, just as insight is largely useless if it is intellectual—rather it should follow from change. Learning of facts or of information as, for instance, how to operate an engine, can be largely intellectual, but learning in the sense it would apply here, that is vital learning, presupposes a change of attitude concerning the whole person. If used in this sense, there appears to be no clear-cut difference between the learning and the therapeutic processes. (For this reason group teaching has special merits. This is also confirmed in psychiatric teaching and it is borne out that experience as a patient—either in individual or group-analytic psychotherapy—has proved to be a powerful means of learning.)

Resistance to Change

Another point should be kept in mind: In psychotherapy as we have it in mind here, and in particular insofar as it is analytic in orientation, the process of *unlearning* is particularly important.

We must never lose sight of the fact that resistances to change, to learning, and to unlearning, are not merely caused by the inherent difficulties in doing so. Even the well-motivated patient—both consciously and unconsciously—has very strong powers working actively in himself against change, a change which would be in his favor. These powerful forces are for the most part unconscious. In the last resort, they must be self-destructive but they are not necessarily so in a straightforward way. It may be, for instance, that the patient is afraid of success or not allowed to enjoy himself. There is as much self-deception operating here as in the case of hidden passionate desires. Projections onto fate or bad luck, onto others, onto the past, are favorite mechanisms. There is also a kind of projection into reality and into the body. On this level, I have in mind real reality ("realization" one might call it) and "real" physical illness, which the doctor or the laboratory test would confirm. Such projections induce other people to act and react in the ways in which the patient anticipated. In the face of such self-deceptions, locating these dark forces within one's own mind is among the most difficult tasks. The profundity of insight required for doing so is given only to few individuals, particularly gifted in this respect.

Strange to say, in my experience, insight sufficient to be workable and effective in practical terms can be achieved not infrequently. Some of the most decisive therapeutic changes occur just in this area. It is here that insight achieves its major triumphs. Since this discussion must be limited, I cannot enter into the theoretical reasons beyond indicating that they stem from the curative agent being not so much the undoing of repression and its allied defense mechanisms as it is the undoing of self-deception in relation to one's own ego identity. A change of heart, of attitude here pays immediate dividends even though the deep sources from which these self-destructive energies flow may remain unconscious.

In addition to all these resistances to change, there is yet another set of resistances which goes beyond the individual as an isolated person. This set leads us to the need for a group pathological and group therapeutic viewpoint as the only appropriate one. The human individual never exists in isolation, least of all in a deep psychological sense. It is as though he had for his well-being, not only to maintain an equilibrium within his own system but also within a system which comprises a number of significant people. These are the representatives of the community and culture in which his life is spent. These representatives may be past or present, physically or otherwise, they may appear to be within or without himself; in their total concert they perform over and over again the tragedy and comedy of love and hatred, of life and death, of all human existence. The individuals are but nodal points in this play of forces and the equilibrium of each is interdependent with that of the others. I like to call this a "network" of interaction. It is inevitable that any change in any one of the members of such a network causes change in any one of the others to a greater or lesser degree and is, therefore, resisted by them. It is not possible here to go further into the consequences of such an insight, both practical and theoretical, and I must refer to some of my own writings concerning this "network" theory of the neuroses and allied disturbances[1, 2]. I believe that this view will ultimately prevail and will provide an end to the distinction between psychology, biology, and sociology, more particularly between "individual" and "social" psychology as well as between psychology and psycho-pathology.

Suffice it here to say that in any individual case this network can be reduced to a relatively few relevant persons. These will almost certainly include members of the family but will most probably not be confined to them. It is in this respect that my network approach differs from the family treatment which has, more recently, begun to come into its own, especially in the United States, but which is nevertheless a step in the right direction. Group treatment that has as its object the therapeutic analysis of such a primary group is one essential form of group psychotherapy. It has great difficulties and holds great dangers as well as promise.

Interaction in Group Psychotherapy

The other major form of group psychotherapy, on the contrary, takes each individual right out of his primary network and mixes him with others, thus forming a new field of interaction in which each individual has a fresh start. The situation is unprejudiced as to his own reactions and contributions as well as those of the other members to himself. He is therefore forced to realize—or to defend himself against such realization—to what extent and depth he is conditioned by imprints of his former and present primary networks. He also has a first-hand opportunity of comparing and contrasting his own ways with those of others; he can see that what he thought peculiar in himself is usual and that what he thought usual is peculiar to him ("mirror reaction"). He also becomes familiar with new ways of suffering and new ways of solution as represented by real persons in the same room with him. This whole new encounter, ever developing and ever changing, is or should be as far as possible, confined to the therapeutic meeting in the presence of the therapist. The therapist's task is to keep the situation thus confined, to keep it therapeutic, that is to say, to preserve individuals from harm through excessive reactions or incompatible selection, to see that what is learned is made meaningful and can be used constructively.

This whole volume is concerned with this second form of group psychotherapy. In the last few sentences, I have only tried to circumscribe some of the essential foundations upon which therapy in groups rests. To go into detail is not my task here, and I can confidently leave that in the hands of the distinguished experts who are your guides.

If we now proceed to our last question, namely, *how* do people change, whether this be generally in life or in this particular situation, we have already given some general answer in the foregoing. A few words may be added: the first condition seems to be experience, vital involved experience, especially in relation to other people.

The therapeutic character of these meetings is personified and maintained by the therapist. I propose that we define clearly the main factors which account for this therapeutic character and, insofar as they are realized, we may call it a T-situation. Such a situation is differently defined according to the material in which we work, including ourselves and our limitations (for example, the time available). The important over-all principle is that our aims are in accordance with these limitations. For our purpose, it is important that the T-situation allows, encourages, and demonstrates repetition of significant behavior and response in transference, that it focuses on the psychological level, gives full recognition to unconscious processes, whether these are manifested intrapersonally or interpersonally. In pure form this can be done in the group-analytic situation, the main ingredient of which is the consistent analytical attitude of the conductor. Only the therapist who is fully trained and experienced as a psychoanalyst and a group analyst can maintain this level and should do so.

However, much valuable group psychotherapy—it may indeed be of greater practical importance—can be done by using the constructive effects of group participation, of didactic influences, and of opening up channels for corrective experiences, which to some extent regulate themselves. This latter type of group psychotherapy leaves the therapist considerable flexibility according to his purpose and inclinations.

In all of these situations it would, however, seem advisable that the therapist does not too readily fulfill the group's wish to be led or to be taught and that he remain relatively nondescript as to his own person. Furthermore, while it is important that newly won and liberated capacities for action and response should be practiced, it is nevertheless necessary to watch that such carrying over into life should not be too hot. Indeed, it is of therapeutic importance to learn *not* to act upon impulses but to keep them in suspense and thus allow for recognition, reflection, and correction. This applies to patient and therapist alike.

Two Types of Groups

It may be useful to keep in mind the two types of groups with which we are concerned:

(*1*) Groups with a task

(*2*) Purely therapeutic groups

Groups with a task may be divided into subgroups (*a*) and (*b*).

Subgroup (*a*) consists of groups in which the task itself is considered important, let us say a team in sport or in industry, in a farming community, or in a hospital where the team works together. In this case, the group is really treated for its own (the group's) sake. Membership in such a group nevertheless has a therapeutic function which is related to the salutory effects of group membership in ordinary life. The group morale, the feeling of doing something together with others, the sharing, the submerging in the common task all have a constructive and therapeutic effect upon its members. However, the individuals joining such a group benefit as a by-product; the group's performance is the real aim.

Subgroup (*b*) consists of groups in which the task is considered unimportant; this may be apparent to the individuals or not. During World War II, for instance, at Northfield Military Hospital, we allowed patients to join different occupational groups at their own wish.[3] They were not in any way told or made aware that we considered their occupations and their achievements in them as unimportant to the therapy. Nevertheless they were. From our point of view, the therapeutic effect on each of the individuals concerned was the really important thing. Incidentally, so far as I know, this was the first time that groups were consciously and deliberately used in this way. In such a group, therefore, it is the individual who counts. The individual improvement or beneficial change is our real interest and the task of the group as such, which is only a provisional *ad hoc* body, is of no importance at all.

The prototype of the second, namely the group without a task, is the group-analytic group.[4] This is sometimes treated by doctors and patients as if they had a task, that of getting well or discussing their problems; but this is implicit rather than explicit and the therapist—as any good leader should—takes his clues from the group's own definition of the situation, in the light of what they do and say or do not do and do not say. In these therapeutic analytic groups it is of course, eventually, the individual alone who counts—a point which is sometimes misunderstood. The analytic group as such has only an *ad hoc* existence as a therapeutic instrument.

In this connection we should remember that many of the groups of the first type, in ordinary life, often use their manifest occupation as a kind of screen which really glosses over the underlying interpersonal problems, sometimes helping them, sometimes covering over the difficulties. It is one of the characteristic features of the group-analytic situation that it takes away this screen function, this occupation, so that its members who are patients can come to the group with their problems, can undress as it were.

The fact that, as was stated, these groups are there only for the individual's treatment must not be confused, as often happens, with ideas and concepts which are important for the orientation of the conductor and for which he needs to consider the total interactional network of his group. There are many special features of the group-analytic situation which I need not, or must not, enter into here. I will present merely a typical example of a group without such a manifest task, a group which is purely devoted to the therapy of the individual.

In the analytic group we wish to go into fundamentals of human life; we wish to face these fundamentals and to submit them to recognition and analysis, bring to the full light of consciousness and scrutiny everything, whether it would be considered otherwise normal or abnormal. The mechanisms with which some people adapt themselves to normality are often on pathological grounds and not even in the best interests of the individual concerned.

To come back to the groups under the first heading (*1,b*), which have a task apart from helping their members by the constructive and supportive morale building, properties of the group can be used for the corrective influence of interaction and frank discussion in a therapeutic milieu.

We can thus help people make their lives at least a little more tolerable. Whether that is a good or a bad thing is not always certain. It may well be that under certain circumstances we only defend their misery when it might be sounder for them to have greater drive for changing things and circumstances rather than themselves. I mention this here as an example of how careful we must be in evaluating what is improvement or only apparent improvement. The therapist should carefully avoid using the group for his own ends and he should correct his own evaluations in the light of those of the group and not the other way around. This should even be true for a politician in a democracy though this may be asking too much.

One last remark. In all these therapeutic encounters, but quite particularly in the analytic setting, it is of course necessary to be frank and truthful. This is difficult at the best of times because the upbringing of men and women in our type of civilization does not always put a premium on truth and the recognition of the reality of a situation. They are, therefore, inclined and conditioned to be dishonest even insofar as they know what is true. In addition, as our experience shows, they do not know just how misled they may be in what they assume to be the truth about themselves.

References

1. FOULKES, S. H., Group processes and the individual in the therapeutic group. *Brit. J. M. Psychol.* 34:23, 1961.
2. FOULKES, S. H., Psychotherapy 1961. *Brit. J. M. Psychol.* 34:91, 1961.
3. FOULKES, S. H., *Introduction to Group-Analytic Psychotherapy: Studies in the Social Integration of Individuals and Groups.* London, Heinemann, and New York, Grune & Stratton, 1948.
4. FOULKES, S. H., and ANTHONY, E. J., *Group Psychotherapy: The Psychoanalytic Approach.* Pelican Psychology Series. London, Penguin, 1957.

the development of group 2
psychotherapy

LONG before man learned to make fire or build a shelter, he had become aware of the special qualities to be derived from gathering together with his fellows. As one result of the interest in and study of these special qualities and of the basic principles underlying group behavior, the group method of psychotherapy developed. One sign of the great growth of group psychotherapy is the constantly increasing volume of literature since Pratt first began to treat the emotional problems arising in his group of tubercular patients[1, 2]. The use of the group technique has spread widely in the half century since Pratt. Group therapy is presently used in many settings and with a great variety of approaches in many diagnostic groups as well as with patients who have many different kinds of problems. It has progressed from being a marginal procedure to being the treatment of choice in many situations.

After the introduction of the group method by Pratt and his followers to cope with the influence of emotions in somatic illnesses, the use of this technique began to spread widely. In 1921, Lazell began to treat dementia praecox by using Pratt's method of lectures and instructions to the patients[3]. Marsh also began to use the lecture technique in classrooms, but expanded this procedure by using loudspeakers to communicate with the total hospital population[4]. There were many

11

other instances of the use of lectures to patients in groups, in attempts to make full use of all available personnel. Snowden's method consisted of eight weekly lectures, in which he would discuss various causes of different mental illnesses for twenty minutes[5]. Following this, patients would get together and discuss the lectures in relationship to their own problems. During the discussion period, the therapist would see each patient individually for a few minutes to point out how the lecture related to his individual problem. Using this method, Snowden was able to help approximately forty persons during the three-hour weekly session within a period of two months. Low[6] and Klapman[7] treated patients by a modified method which emphasized group interviews rather than lectures and recitals.

Psychoanalytically Oriented Groups

The first reported attempts to utilize psychoanalytic concepts in group psychotherapy were made by Trigant Burrow[8]. His method of treatment was based on the theory that people lived in and were part of a society and that isolation of the individual in treatment actually may destroy his relatedness with his group or society. He said of the group method: "This comprehensive scheme of analysis has the merit of leaving intact the material of our societal and instinctual group life, while at the same time it proceeds from this group background to examine analytically the social, as well as the personal substitutions and repressions embodied in the arbitrary collective sum or pseudogroup represented in this selfsame societal organism"[9]. Burrow found that all material which was verbalized in individual analysis (*e.g.*, sexual fantasies, family conflicts), was also verbalized in even relatively large groups. He found manifestations of transference relationships and defense mechanisms, as well as other traditional dimensions of individual psychoanalysis.

Burrow felt that the greatest value of the group was its potential for diminishing patient resistance to the treatment process. As the patient became aware that his problem was not unique, he lost the need to maintain secrecy and isolation. The loss of this need helped to resolve the patient's resistance. Burrow emphasized that man was not an individual but a societal organism and should be treated as such. "In my interpretation, the group method of analysis is but the application in the phylogenetic sphere of the individual analysis as first applied by Freud without the ontogenetic sphere"[10]. He placed the need for greater emphasis on *"immediate material"* with a proportionate disregard for reminiscences. At roughly the same period as Burrow, Kurt Lewin in Germany was developing the concepts of field theory and group dynamics that have so substantially contributed to the creation of modern social psychology[11].

In the early 1930's, Louis Wender began to utilize psychoanalytically oriented group therapy in a hospital setting[12]. His use of the group method was in response to a need to develop treatment for certain types of mild mental diseases. He utilized the group method in combination with individual interviews and found that patients spoke more freely and brought out more conflictual material at individual sessions when they were also in group psychotherapy. Although Wender utilized psychoanalytic concepts in his group, his sessions began with lecture materials on subjects such as why individuals behaved as they did, drives, the conscious and unconscious, and the significance of dreams. Transference relationships were found between patient and therapist and among patients. As the group continued, the patient's spontaneity increased and he was able to discuss his own problems in relation to the theoretical material presented. Dreams were discussed and interpreted on a superficial level. Wender found that the drive for getting well was greater in the group than in individual psychotherapy.

Paul Schilder also began to use the group method as a psychotherapeutic technique in the early 1930's[13]. He reported that patients' ideologies were built around and developed from the self or body image. Psychotherapy enabled the patient to see that his convictions had little basis in fact. The patient was forced to ask himself how he came to accept this particular ideology and how it gained such an influence over his actions. Schilder emphasized that the patient's ideas and convictions were part of his life in the community and that it was very logical to discuss the ideologies of one patient in front of the group. This tended to clarify the issue and bring it to the group's attention. The discussion was likely to start on an intellectual level and lead to the person's private life experiences. This procedure took the problem out of the realm of the individual and lessened the patient's feeling of being an isolate. When other patients in the group were able to identify with the problem, they were better able to work on and resolve it. Schilder stated that the therapist had to believe that intellectual honesty is a necessary prerequisite for psychotherapy. The group therapist has to take an active part with a willingness to reveal his own ideology and justify it before the group.

The Group Method in England

The group method was also being practiced in England during the 1930's. One of the most active experimenters was Joshua Bierer at the Runwell Hospital for Nervous and Mental Diseases[14]. Bierer engaged in "situational treatment," the goal of which was not the acquisition of knowledge about the "subconscious." Instead, the goal was a living experience which would result in a change in attitude. Bierer believed that the "social club" was the first step to make the patient change from being an "*object*" to being a "subject." The activities of such a club included entertaining, sports, writing, painting, and discussions. The groups met once a week with the therapist to discuss personal problems in what could be called an impersonal way. The therapist usually took a passive role. At the club at Runwell, composed of 50–100 people, about ten got together on a weekly basis in a "circle," in which they discussed one patient's problems in an impersonal way. Bierer stressed that it was even better if the patient did not know that his problems were being discussed. It was during these discussion periods that individuals were able to identify and work through their own problems. Bierer saw several advantages in such situational therapy: (*1*) It bridged the gulf between insight and cure which exists in individual psychoanalysis. (This is similar to the philosophy of Burrow.) (*2*) The patients in the hospital become more independent, active, and self-deciding, which hastens their cure. (*3*) It makes it easier for the patient to solve social problems which create conflict for him in the outside world.

S. H. Foulkes, a world leader in group psychotherapy, founded the Group-Analytic Society and established a program in group psychotherapy at the Maudsley Hospital in London[15, 16]. In 1940, Foulkes was the first person in the British Isles to practice group psychotherapy on a psychoanalytic basis. When World War II came, Foulkes utilized his group psychotherapy techniques with the British armed forces.

As a result of his war experiences, he expressed the belief that group therapy was an expression of a new attitude toward the study and improvement of human relationships. He stressed the point that this method also may be viewed as "an instrument, perhaps the first adequate one, for a practical approach to the key problem of our time: The strained relationship between the individual and the community"[17].

Foulkes has continued the exploration and further development of group psychotherapy within the framework of classic psychoanalytic theory. He has stressed the importance of consistency in the procedure of conducting psychotherapeutic group sessions. He notes that variations in group procedures tend to create many variables, which make it extremely difficult to examine what is happening in the analytic process. He has stressed the desirability of using a strictly defined method for the purpose of exchanging experiences and also for research, although his practice has stressed the flexibility and variation that particular situations may require. In relationship to restrictions, Foulkes emphasizes that restrictions eliminate variables. The patient has to accept the role of a patient and has to *bear* it in the hour of analysis. People tend to deviate and it is most important that group psychotherapists standardize the settings and procedures. "We have to know what we actually are doing—then we can understand the results of what we are doing. Devise simple situations and stick to them."

In his theoretical framework and practice of group psychotherapy, Foulkes tends to limit variations within the group in relationship to age, *e.g.*, 18–25, 25–35, and 35–55. The patients are also selected in relationship to I.Q. levels. He tends to select patients with high intellectual endowment, I.Q. 110–125+. Although he has reported considerable success with conversion hysterics, he has noted that a whole group or majority of conversionals offers particularly difficult resistances, and may be more difficult to treat or cure than patients with other diagnoses usually considered much more deeply disturbed. He also believes that "headache" patients are most difficult in a group. Many have severe difficulty in facing up to their total problems and tend to "prop up" the nonunderstanding and nonaccepting of total analysis. Foulkes has trained many psychoanalysts in group procedures and has been extraordinarily influential.

Some American Pioneers

S. R. Slavson, a pioneer and the most driving force behind American analytic group psychotherapy, can be considered the most prolific contributor to the professional literature. He originated and developed Activity Group Therapy[18]. Slavson studied the psychodynamics of children with character disorders in a setting in which many manual activities contributed to the matrix of treatment. This therapeutic method involved bringing about positive attachments to group members and the therapist and eventually to persons in the outside environment. Results were partially attributed to the permissive atmosphere where the children could act out hostile and aggressive feelings without being punished.

Slavson continued his work by expanding his theories of psychotherapy in groups to adults[19]. It is Slavson's concept that the common elements in all sound psychotherapies, including analytic group psychotherapy, are: (1) relation (transference); (2) catharsis; (3) insight; (4) reality testing; and (5) sublimation. It is his belief that individual psychotherapy, although supplying the first three elements, does not supply the latter two as part of the treatment situation. Group therapy, on the other hand, supplies all five of these elements. Within the group situation, various types of relations may lead to mutual support, to the possible discharge of aggression or the assuaging of guilt feelings. The characteristic clusters and subgrouping that tend to develop within the large therapeutic group offer definite value to each of the participants. Depending on the specific situation, transference within the group occurs in cycles. Both positive and negative feelings may be intensified through indentification and rivalry. Rivalry may manifest itself when the patients attempt to please the therapist, and in so doing, secure his attention and love. Because the latent hostile and aggressive feelings toward the parental figures are almost always near the surface and easily activated, feelings of guilt and the need for group protection against punishment tend to create a bond amongst the patients. It is within the negative phases of the transference relationships that group unity is most evident.

Concerning the functions of the therapist, Slavson believes that he must have adequate information of the psychodynamics and psychopathology of each person in the group and must know the nuclear problem of each. The therapist should have sufficient information in order to determine the course of treatment which is to be followed with each patient and the depth of the treatment necessary, *e.g.*, will he deal with basic conflicts or will he work with behavioral and attitudinal manifestations. Further, the therapist must be constantly aware of the latent content and the direction of the group interviews. The knowledge of each participant's psychodynamics will allow him to help the patients overcome their differences and fear through appropriate use of the transference and ego support.

Another pioneer is J. L. Moreno, among whose many contributions was the introduction of the term "group psychotherapy" in 1932. Moreno has developed a theory of group structure as well as a method of group therapy and has been a very prolific contributor to the professional literature[20]. His chosen instruments for psychotherapy are psychodrama and sociodrama. Psychodrama is a procedure whereby one or more persons with problems interacts with others, but takes varied roles. In sociodrama the patients are the audience. Moreno believes that man is spontaneous and creative by nature, but becomes sick if he cannot use this natural endowment. He uses groups in order to help persons to discover their lost spontaneity. Spontaneous stage play became the medium of dramatic expression by which patients could act out their conflicts. Acting out rather than talking out, according to his view, could lead to deep catharsis of self limiting forces and free the patient's creativity. Each actor-patient thus became a self healing as well as a therapeutic agent to other patients.

Recognizing the dire need for an economical form of psychoanalytic treatment, Alexander Wolf began practicing "psychoanalysis in groups" around 1939[21]. He demonstrated that psychoanalytic concepts and methods could be translated into a group setting. He originated the alternate session, which is a regularly scheduled group session without the therapist. The alternate sessions had the advantage of making it easier for some patients to express themselves. It also provided the group members an opportunity to function as a group outside the direct dependency relationship with the prototypical parental figure of the therapist.

The Group Method in Various Settings

The group method of treatment is utilized in governmental and private mental hospitals, general hospitals, outpatient clinics, social agencies, schools, as well as in private practice settings. The specific use of the group method often varies even within the same setting, since it is dependent upon the aim and goals of both therapist and patients. One of the important outgrowths of the therapeutic method is a tendency toward organization of mental hospitals on the basis of group participation[22]. Rees and Glatt, two exponents of this procedure, have noted that: "We believe that the most satisfactory, as well as the most practical way of organizing the mental hospital as a therapeutic community, is one based on group therapy, including occupational and recreational therapy"[23]. It is their belief that the patient's conflicts are likely to be precipitated by his relationships with others in society and he has a better opportunity of clarifying such relationships in group participation. Many mental institutions have developed treatment programs which include group psychotherapy for psychotic patients and group counseling with patients' relatives, as well as group treatment of the patient together with his family. The treatment of families now includes all members of the family being seen as members of the same therapy group[24]. Parents and children work through their individual intrapsychic conflicts as well as the family's interpersonal difficulties.

The group method of treatment has also become a means of preventive mental health in many settings. General hospitals, community treatment centers, and other agencies have begun group programs to treat patients with problems like obesity and gastrointestinal disorders. Group treatment of alcoholics, drug addicts, and parents of handicapped children, has been reported. Some community as well as social agencies have developed group programs to treat juvenile delinquents. Modified forms of group therapy are now being used to treat emotionally disturbed children in camp settings. Guidance groups may be found in child guidance clinics as well as in the treatment of adults. Many other settings have used different kinds of group psychotherapy.

Variations of the kind of therapeutic social clubs which were originally organized by Bierer in London are now being used in both inpatient and outpatient settings. Cameron has been a leading spokesman for the psychiatric day hospital which stresses group therapy[25]. Various day hospitals have had successes utilizing social activity by the group members[26]. Some groups are and others are not followed by a discussion period. The daily activity and institutional interaction of the group members are ventilated. This procedure faciliates translation of patient's object relations into verbal communication. These groups have had excellent results in helping the affect-withdrawn patients with severe difficulty in relating to others.

Some patients who had been almost completely withdrawn have been helped to re-establish contact with reality and to establish interpersonal relationships by use of the "remotivational technique" developed by Smith[27]. The patient is placed in a group and the therapist tries to stimulate the patient to react to nature stimuli like sand, grass, and flowers. Following the identification of the objects, the patient is asked to give his association to them. Other persons in the group are gradually drawn into the discussion and associations. The continuing responses and associations to the encouragement and aid of the therapist result in interaction among the patients. Music has been used successfully in groups as a stimulus in helping other withdrawn patients to communicate within and to the group[28].

Guidance and Counseling Groups

Groups have been used for guidance purposes. Such groups are problem-centered and their goal is to make it possible for each individual to function better in his life situation. The group stimulates discussion and also tends to increase patients' ego strength through the acceptance of other members, as well as by identification of problems. The guidance groups of college students who, although having high intellectual potentials, function very poorly in their academic work, are an example of this form of help. Although each member of the group presents features of different neurotic problems and symptomatology, the focus of the sessions is the members' common problem of difficulty in both applying themselves and attaining their academic goals. The group leader stimulates and encourages open discussion of universal, common, and individual problems which might lend themselves to creation of cohesiveness among the members. As the members become involved in the discussion, they begin to express conflicts which have created the anxiety which, in turn, have prevented sustained effort in their academic studies. As the sessions progress, the members begin to see some communality in their problems and so are able to identify with one another. Childhood experiences with parents and siblings which the students feel contribute to their difficulties are discussed. On occasion, transference relationships begin to emerge and the group leader immediately interprets these, in order to diminish the possible eruption of intense anxiety. The leader focuses all discussions on their relevance to the problem of the academic difficulties. The discussions during the sessions provide each member with an opportunity to understand and accept the others and in so doing, to understand and accept themselves. Ego strength is increased, enabling them to formulate and carry through corrective measures.

Counseling in groups is another group therapeutic direction which has been found to be useful. The therapy in such groups is ego-oriented. Problems and feelings are freely discussed, but the discussions are more concerned with significant people outside the group constellation than they are with the people who are in the group. Transference relationships among the members are kept at a minimum through ignoring them or having definite rules that all discussions are to center around common problems rather than personal feelings toward one another. One such group is that of parents of physically handicapped children. Another example is that of parents of cerebral-palsied children, as reported by Boles[29]. In this group, the first several sessions focused primarily on practical problems and feelings surrounding experiences with the children. The parents expressed many previously pent-up feelings of anger and resentment against what they had felt to be injustices experienced with physicians, neighbors, school, and community as a whole. As the meetings continued, the group members began to explore more personal areas, which included reactions of shock and shame, self-blame and guilt, as well as death wishes towards the handicapped child. As the sessions progressed, the individual parent realized that he was not unique in his problem, that he was not to be blamed for the tragedy of the physical handicap of his child. With the working through of the anxieties and guilt, the parents were better able to accept their children as individuals rather than an affliction.

In psychotherapy groups with psychoanalytic orientation, the working through of conflicts on a deeper level is the goal. Utilization of the multiple transference relationships explores id impulses, ego strength and super-ego restrictions. In these forms of group treatment, free associations, dreams, and fantasies are used as material for discussion and exploration.

Relationship of Group Dynamics to Group Psychotherapy

The application of the principles of group dynamics to the therapeutic group is an issue which continues to be debated. There are eloquent statements of each of the several points of view in this debate[30]. Foulkes[31] and Ezriel[32] in England, as well as Frank[33], Bach[34], and Durkin[35] in America, assume in varying degrees that group dynamics may be utilized in the therapeutic group. Taking the opposite position are such writers as Slavson[36], McCormack[37], and most extensively, Wolf and Schwartz[38]. The latter writers point out that group dynamics may be used in schools, industrial plants, club work, but not in therapy. They stress that making group dynamics central tends to diminish psychotherapeutic processes in the group. Foulkes[31] and Durkin[35] have attempted to breach the seeming dichotomy of group therapy-group dynamics. Durkin states that all types of groups may be comparable because they have a common dynamic basis in psychology of ego interaction[35]. It is her belief that group and therapeutic forces are on the whole mutually reenforcing, but at times may work in opposite directions. Foulkes and Spotnitz[39] have independently noted that every event in the group involves the group as a whole, even though seemingly confined to one or two participants. Foulkes and Anthony write, "Such events are part of a gestalt, configuration, of which they constitute the figures (foreground), whereas the ground (background) is manifested in the rest of the group. We have described as *location* the process which brings to life this concealed configuration; it is, however, not always a simple matter to locate this pattern in the group's reaction [p. 9]"[16].

Since the individual is a social being who is a product of environmental as well as of intrapsychic forces and biological drives, the group would appear to be a natural setting for experiencing and working through interpersonal as well as intrapersonal conflicts. Within the group, the person is able to establish and communicate on a one-to-one relationship. As a group member, he may re-experience a familial constellation, whether it be his nuclear family or some other group or groups. As the individual communicates in the group the therapist is able to observe his patterns of behavior to others and how they are influenced by the varying stimuli provided by the group. The therapeutic process almost always results in the development of the special kind of relationship called transference. Within the group setting, the relationships of the patient may not only develop with the therapist but may also develop with other group members. Each relationship is developed and is constantly influenced by the existence and pressures of the patient's other relationships.[40]

The use of group psychotherapy has been accepted by adherents of various analytic groups. During the plenary session of the annual conferences of the American Group Psychotherapy Association in 1956, various persons discussed the views of the classical Freudian, Adlerian, Jungian, and Horney schools in relationship to group psychotherapy. Although each school tended to have a different emphasis, all in varying degrees have accepted the group process as promoting therapeutic progress.

References

1. PRATT, J. H., The class method of treating consumption in the homes of the poor. *J.A.M.A. 49:*755, 1907.
2. PRATT, J. H., Results obtained in the treatment of pulmonary tuberculosis by the class method. *Brit. M. J.* 2:1070, 1908.
3. LAZELL, E. W., The group treatment of dementia praecox. *Psychoanalyt. Rev.* 8:168, 1921.
4. MARSH, L. C., Group treatment of the psychoses by the psychological equivalent of the revival. *Ment. Hyg.* 15:328, 1931.
5. SNOWDEN, E. L., Mass Psychotherapy. *Lancet* 2:769, 1940.
6. LOW, A. A., Group psychotherapy. *Ill. Psychiat. J.* 1:3, 1941.
7. KLAPMAN, J. W., *Group Psychotherapy, Theory and Practice.* New York, Grune and Stratton, 1946.
8. BURROW, T., The group method of analysis. *Psychoanalyt. Rev. 14:*268, 1926.
9. *Ibid.*, p. 271.
10. *Ibid.*, p. 279.
11. LEWIN, K., *Dynamic Theory of Personality.* New York, McGraw-Hill, 1936.
12. WENDER, L., The dynamics of group psychotherapy and its application. *J. Nerv. & Ment. Dis.* 84:54, 1936.
13. SCHILDER, P., The analysis of ideologies as a psychotherapeutic method, especially in group treatment. *Am. J. Psychiat.* 93:601, 1936.
14. BIERER, J., Group psychotherapy. *Brit. M. J.* 1:214, 1942.

15. FOULKES, S. H., *Introduction to Group-Analytic Psychotherapy*. New York, Grune & Stratton, 1948.
16. FOULKES, S. H., and ANTHONY, E. J., *Group Psychotherapy: The Psychoanalytic Approach*. Baltimore, Penguin, 1957.
17. FOULKES, S. H., On group psychoanalysis. *Internat. J. Psycho. Analysis* 27:51, 1946.
18. SLAVSON, S. R., *An Introductory to Group Therapy*. New York, Commonwealth Fund, 1943.
19. SLAVSON, S. R., *Analytic Group Psychotherapy*. New York, Columbia Univ. Press, 1950.
20. MORENO, J. L., Group psychotherapy, theory and practice. *Group Psychotherapy* 3:142, 1950.
21. WOLF, A., The psychoanalysis of groups. *Am. J. Psychotherapy* 3:525, 1949; 4:16, 1950.
22. REES, T. P., and GLATT, M. M., The organization of a mental hospital on the basis of group participation. *Internat. J. Group Psychotherapy* 4:154, 1955.
23. *Ibid.*, p. 157.
24. ACKERMAN, N. W., *The Dynamics of Family Treatment*. New York, Basic, 1959.
25. CAMERON, D. E., The day hospital. *Mod. Hosp.* 69:60, 1947.
26. WINICK, C., Psychiatric day hospitals: a survey. *J. Soc. Issues* 16:9, 1960.
27. SMITH, D. H., *Remotivation* (Motion Pic. Film). Philadelphia, Smith, Kline & French.
28. WINICK, C., and HOLT, H., Uses of music in group psychotherapy. *Group Psychotherapy* 13:76, 1960.
29. BOLES, G., Simultaneous group therapy with cerebral-palsied children and their parents. *Internat. J. Group Psychotherapy* 9:488, 1960.
30. Symposium, group dynamics and group psychodynamics. *Internat. J. Group Psychotherapy* 7:3, 1957.
31. FOULKES, S. H., Group analytic dynamics with specific reference to psychoanalytic concepts. *Internat. J. Group Psychotherapy* 7:40, 1957.
32. EZRIEL, H., Notes on psychoanalytic group therapy: II interpretation and research. *Psychiatry* 15:119, 1952.
33. FRANK, J. D., Some determinants, manifestations and effects of cohesiveness in therapy groups. *Internat. J. Group Psychotherapy* 7:53, 1957.
34. BACH, G. R., Observations on transference and object relations in the light of group dynamics. *Internat. J. Group Psychotherapy* 7:64, 1957.
35. DURKIN, H. E., Towards a common basis for group dynamics: group and therapeutic processes in group psychotherapy. *Internat. J. Group Psychotherapy* 7:115, 1957.
36. SLAVSON, S. R., Are there 'group dynamics' in therapy groups? *Internat. J. Group Psychotherapy* 7:131, 1957.
37. McCORMACK, C. G., Group dynamics: homeopathic treatment. *Internat. J. Group Psychotherapy* 7:103, 1957.
38. WOLF, A., and SCHWARTZ, E. K., "Psychoanalysis in Groups: The Mystique of Group Dynamics." *Topical Problems of Psychotherapy*, Basel, 1960, Vol. 2, p. 119.
39. SPOTNITZ, H., The borderline schizophrenic in group psychotherapy. *Internat. J. Group Psychotherapy* 7:155, 1957.
40. SCHEIDLINGER, S. *Psychoanalysis and Group Behavior*. New York, Norton, 1952.

developing a group 3
therapy program

THE development of a group therapy program, institutional or private, requires much consideration and planning. The decision to conduct group therapy in a particular setting is only a first step. No matter how convinced one is that group methods can be successfully applied as a psychotherapeutic technique, it is necessary to have such a program understood by those who are responsible for it or will help implement it. In institutions there is almost always a professional hierarchy which must be considered. In private practice, the therapist may follow his own convictions, but he must anticipate that he will have to educate his sources of referral about the selection of members of the groups. These are situations in which there is great merit in careful preparation of the people directly or indirectly concerned. The type and degree of preparation will not only affect initial cooperation in starting the program, but will color later experience.

Introducing Group Therapy

In institutions, whether hospital, clinic, agency, or school, there is usually an existing and systematized integrated treatment procedure with prescribed roles for the staff. The therapist interested in introducing a group therapy program is usually confronted with a formidable task in integrating his plans within the existing framework. In considering any innovation, like the introduction of group psychotherapy, the administration of the institution usually is concerned with three aspects: (1) economy; (2) effectiveness; (3) personnel. Administrators are sometimes uninformed or misinformed about the advantages, disadvantages, and staff requirements, as well as the space requirements for group psychotherapy. The space requirements are minimal, consisting of a room and comfortable chairs for each of the patients, therapist, co-therapist, and observers who may be sitting in with the group, if they are included in the therapeutic team.

One major dimension of group psychotherapy is its economy in terms of patient needs, time, staff, and money. A major concern of many mental health institutions is a long waiting list. Utilizing individual therapy alone, each therapist is restricted to a limited number of patients he can see. Even if the therapy session is limited to thirty minutes, he is able to see only two patients an hour. In group therapy, eight to twelve patients may be seen by one staff member at the same time. Considering that the group session is often an extended one, sometimes lasting two hours, the therapist is able to see an average of four to six patients per hour. The group therapist's ability to see a relatively large number of patients in a limited time can appreciably reduce the waiting list for treatment at clinics and other institutional settings.

Group therapy has been successfully conducted by professionals from different backgrounds. The leader for a group may be a well-trained psychiatrist, psychologist, social worker, or a representative of other disciplines, depending upon the particular goal for the group. It is even possible for an adequately trained attendant and nurse to work with a group of withdrawn isolates in a situation where the goal is remotivation, in an attempt to bring such patients into closer contact with their surroundings.

Each patient setting is likely to have its own treatment goals. The group method has many applications and may be utilized to meet the specific needs which are encountered in a particular setting. The method is applicable to almost all age groups and to many different treatment goals. Group methods may be used for intensive analytic group psychotherapy, for guidance, and counseling. Group methods have successfully been used with parents, married couples, persons awaiting assignment for psychotherapy, withdrawn isolates and for others who are not suitable candidates for individual therapy. Group therapy is a socio-psychological experience which may increase the patient's confidence and reduce anxiety. Treatment effectiveness may also be gauged by the extent to which the group program renders the patient more acceptable to other patients and better able to profit from other therapeutic approaches like medication, occupational, and individual psychotherapy. Critical reality problems are usually voiced in group sessions, placing the therapist in the advantageous position of being able to cope with these issues in terms of patient needs and/or resistances.

Each institutional setting usually has its own departmental structure. Staff members carry out prescribed functions with what is often minimum contact with other therapeutic personnel. Staff role delineations may be a source of friction, especially when they are hierarchical. The group therapy program may do much to dispel sources of staff conflict and tension. It unites professionals of various backgrounds in a mutual treatment enterprise. It facilitates communication among staff members, and may tend to enhance mutual trust. However, a group treatment plan may offend certain staff members, especially those committed to a particular treatment approach or who experience a threat to their own position. This conflict is often overcome with the passage of time and education, and may be accompanied by significant gains in staff morale. As there is growing knowledge of the group program on the part of the therapeutic staff, communication about the program is likely to become more informal. The group approach fosters an enrichment of knowledge about patients which may be communicated to other staff members, no matter what the professional background.

To aid the person who plans to inaugurate group psychotherapy in an institutional setting, it may be advantageous to consider some schematic considerations. The following are some general questions and answers which represent typical situations.

QUESTION: Will this program constitute an economic burden?

ANSWER: The physical plant requirements for group psychotherapy are minimal. All that is required is a room and enough chairs to seat the participants in the group. The group method of treatment may be used in both adults' and children's departments. The only additional physical requirements would be occasioned by the specialized technique of activity therapy, which entails a special workshop setting. Using group therapy, more patients may be treated within a limited time. Where a fee is paid for treatment, the individual may pay less and at the same time the total income for the time spent is higher than in individual therapy, e.g., four individual patients seen in a period of two hours at $5.00 each is an average of $10.00 per hour, as compared to eight patients in a group at $3.00 each in a group session lasting two hours, averaging $12.00 per hour. In a setting where the patient does not pay for the treatment, waiting lists may be substantially reduced. The number and diagnostic variety of patients who are able to receive treatment is increased.

QUESTION: Does the effectiveness of group psychotherapy warrant its utilization?

ANSWER: The group method may be used for analytic psychotherapy, guidance, counseling, and combined psychotherapy for all ages. In a hospital setting, various forms of group treatment are most effective in remotivating isolates, withdrawn, autistic patients. It acts as an invaluable aid to individual therapeutic endeavors (psychotherapy, chemotherapy, and electrotherapy). The group may also be utilized as a means of orientation, reducing the intense apprehension and anxiety related to confinement. Prior to termination of hospitalization, the group offers the patient an opportunity for experiencing, expressing, and working through interpersonal sociopsychological problems anticipated when he returns to his own home and community.

The group may also be used as a means of working with the family of the hospitalized patient. Once the patient has left the hospital, follow-up treatment in a group has often proved very successful and effective. In an outpatient setting, many of the values of the inpatient setting are also present. Various types of guidance groups may be instituted. Fulfilling an important function are therapy-social clubs, functioning on the basis of the club originated in London by Bierer. Psychodrama also has an effective place in a group therapy program in an institutional setting. This technique is especially effective with patients who have special difficulties with verbal communication and find it easier to express themselves through movement.

QUESTION: How will such a program affect the staff?

ANSWER: The initial response of the individual therapist may be one of great interest, but may also be negative and critical. The latter reaction may be especially so if the therapist feels that his patient may be incorporated into a group, and as such be a reflection of his inadequate therapeutic skills. The group therapy program, however, may in fact be a very valuable aid to the individual therapist. Many a therapist has patients who have failed to show progressive movement for a relatively long period. As therapeutic sessions become unproductive, both therapist and patient may develop an attitude of boredom and disinterest. For these patients, as well as the therapist, the group may represent an invigorating stimulus. If the resistive patient enters combined individual and group treatment, the individual sessions often become more productive and movement is made possible by this change of therapeutic milieu. Such considerations may be encouraging to the individual therapist who is chary of group therapy.

QUESTION: How can the cooperation of the personnel be enlisted to develop a group program?

ANSWER: With the consent of the appropriate administrative officers, specifics of the group program may be communicated in detail. The immediate task for the group therapist is to facilitate the flow of patients for group therapy, specifically those from other units or other therapists. It is particularly important to make the goals of group therapy meaningful to the sources of referral.

One of the most effective means of attaining positive results in getting across the ideas of a group program is to communicate these ideas at a general staff conference. The meeting should be conducted in such a manner as to offer the staff an opportunity to ventilate all possible objections. These objections may be viewed and dealt with as realistic queries, and sometimes as resistances resulting from lack of knowledge. The entire staff may be enlisted to participate in bringing out and resolving anticipated problems and threats to the individual staff member. In the discussion of using group method as a placement technique, the staff members may be invited to orientation sessions. At such sessions, patients may be observed to determine their amenability to psychotherapy. Selection of the particular treatment method may be made during this period. The therapist may gain knowledge and insight into the patients and select for individual therapy those patients with whom he feels he can be most effective. Patients who may immediately go into group or combined (group plus individual) treatment may be selected according to the criteria and goals of specific groups that are being formed.

Conflicts of interest may also be worked out in the staff conference, although group therapy usually facilitates rather than interferes with other therapeutic techniques. Timing of group sessions may be established in order not to interfere with occupational, individual psychotherapeutic, medicinal, or other treatment plans. Nurses, occupational therapists, and attendants may be invited to attend group sessions over a specified period as participating or silent observers. In this capacity they may gain knowledge about patients' conflicts and problems and increase understanding in helping the individual patient cope adequately with them. Post-meeting discussions with the observer help cement his understanding of the patients' underlying psychodynamics which are manifested in the actions and interactions taking place in the group sessions. These auxiliary personnel may be further stimulated and encouraged by a discussion and inclusion of social and motivational techniques and their benefits to the patients.

One consideration in introducing group therapy is its effect on the therapist who is conducting the individual therapy. When two or more persons are involved in the treatment of an individual, they form an integral team which is able to offer a great deal of learning to each of its members. Written communication among the team members may be continued, but usually becomes a stimulus for verbal discussion. During these usually informal discussion periods, each team member is not only able to broaden his knowledge but also to see how theory and practice are related.

QUESTION: How do you go about getting a group therapy program started?

ANSWER: The actual initiation of a group psychotherapy program in an institutional setting, whether inpatient or outpatient, is dependent upon the needs of the setting, as well as the goal of this therapeutic procedure. Audiovisual techniques are both impressive and instructive. Films may be viewed and studied and then shown to the staff, with elaboration and group discussion. The developer of the group program may invite competent outside lecturers who can clarify the methods and advantages of group treatment for the particular setting. Following the film and lecture, there might be a general discussion for the entire staff, including attendants, nurses, and other auxiliary personnel.

Following the initial introduction, other meetings may be organized and arranged. It is most advantageous to have these meetings take the form of small workshops which focus on special facets of the total program. One group might discuss the problems and possible solutions in relation to an over-all treatment plan. A second group might discuss the advantages of an intake group. Another workshop might discuss the existing therapeutic problems within the institution and how different groups constellations might aid in coping with these situations. Each of the workshops should also acquaint itself with criteria for selection of patients who might advantageously benefit from group therapy and the placement of these patients in different group constellations. Intake personnel have a role of utmost importance in any setting, and as such should allocate special time to study the waiting list, as well as patients who have been undergoing treatment for an extended period of time.

QUESTION: What kinds of films on group therapy are available?

ANSWER: There are a number of films on group therapy that should be useful in terms of professional education. There are a number of publications that list such films[1-3]. There is a central registry of film libraries from which these films may be borrowed or rented[4].

At the Board of Directors' meeting held during the 1962 annual conferences of the American Group Psychotherapy Association, the Audio-Visual Committee, under the chairmanship of Asya L. Kadis, presented through its secretary, Dr. Josephine H. Ross, a compilation of films and tapes on group psychotherapy which are available for training purposes. The films which are included in this report follow:

Activity Group Therapy (16 mm.) Running time: 1 hour. Type of group: latency boys. Setting: Child Guidance Clinic. Type of treatment: activity group therapy, developed by S. R. Slavson. A selected group of eight boys were filmed for a period of two years by concealed cameras. Changes were recorded visually, and discussed in clinical conferences or staff, including psychiatrists, psychiatric social workers, and group therapists. Year made: 1950. Produced by Jewish Board of Guardians under direction of S. R. Slavson. Time available: indefinite. Shipped by mail. Cost of renting: $10.00 first day, $5.00 each successive day. Restricted to *clinical* audience. Contact: Film Library, Yeshiva University, 526 West 187 Street, New York City, New York.

A Demonstration of Psychodramatic Techniques (16 mm.) Running time: 30 minutes. Type of group: volunteer adults in demonstration TV session. Type of treatment: psychodramatic. Includes 15 minutes of pre-planned demonstration of psychodramatic technique and 15 minutes spontaneous group activity. Part of series winning Lasker Award. Year made: 1960. Produced by: KNOX-TV (CBS affiliate). Shipped by parcel post. Cost of borrowing: mailing expenses. Unrestricted as to audience. Contact: either A. G. Ossorio, Ph.D., Chief Psychologist, or Leon Fine, Director, Psychodrama and Group Psychotherapy, St. Louis State Hospital, 5400 Arsenal Street, St. Louis, Missouri.

Group Therapy with Alcoholics (16 mm.) Running time: 25 minutes. Type of group: adult males. Setting: outpatient clinic in university psychiatric hospital. Type of treatment: nondirective and supportive. 37th session of open-end group, continuous and unedited. Introduction, comments and summary by Dr. Clancy geared to acquaint physicians in general practice with treatment of alcoholism. Year made: 1961. Produced by Alcoholic Clinic, State Psychiatric Hospital, State University, Iowa City, Iowa.

Introduction to Psychodrama (16 mm.) Running time: 27 minutes. Type of group: unrestricted. Can be used didactically. Type of treatment: unrehearsed, spontaneous, short scenes with commentary. Year made: 1948. Produced by J. L. Moreno and associates. Time available: as needed. Shipped by mail. Cost of borrowing: $10.00 per showing, plus 75¢ for shipping. Unrestricted as to audience. Contact: J. L. Moreno, M.D., 259 Wolcott Avenue, Beacon, New York.

Let There Be Light (16 mm.) Running time: 1 hour. Setting: Mason General Hospital. Made during World War II of treatment in the Army's chief psychiatric center. Film designed to bring out an emotional appreciation of the nature of emotional disorders, their progress and treatment. A documentary of 3 months of treatment with patients constantly filmed, with no acting or planning. Final film reduction of this material. Produced by U. S. Army, Director, John Huston; camera work, Stanley Cortez. Restricted by War Department for professional audience only, and in presence of Benjamin Simon, M.D., formerly Chief of Neuropsychiatry and Executive Officer of Mason General Hospital, *who must be present to deal with the discussion.* Contact: Benjamin Simon, M.D., 53 State Road, Boston 15, Massachusetts.

Role Playing in Guidance (16 mm.) Running time: 14 minutes. Type of group: adults. Setting: private counselor. Type of treatment: psychodramatic. A case study illustrating how role-playing is handled by a teacher-counselor trained in the use of psychodramatic techniques. The film suggests the range of modern action-methods available for dealing with real-life problems. Year made: 1960. Produced by University of California at Los Angeles, Department of Visual Communication. Time available: to be arranged with Public Film Rental Library. Shipped by prepaid carrier. Cost of borrowing: $3.50. No restrictions as to audience. Contact: Educational Film Sales, University Extension, University of California, Berkeley 4, California.

Remotivation: A New Technique for the Psychiatric Aide (16 mm.) Running time: 24 minutes. Type of group: adult. Setting: mental hospital. Type of treatment: supportive group interaction, as part of over-all patient therapy. Actual remotivation session in action, with commentaries, describing technique, benefits, and methods. Year made: 1958. Produced by Smith, Kline & French Laboratories. Time available: any period. Shipped by parcel post. Cost of borrowing: free (except for return postage). Unrestricted as to audience, but generally shown to physicians, nurses, psychiatric attendants, and others directly concerned with mental health. Contact: Reade B. Nimick, Service Section, Smith, Kline & French, 1500 Spring Garden Street, Philadelphia 1, Pennsylvania.

Tape recordings of various group psychotherapy lectures and sessions included in the report are:

Benjamin, Henry, M.D., "Group Psychotherapy." (3 tapes) Type of group: adults, male and female. Setting: state hospital. Type of treatment: supportive, nondirective. Consecutive sessions. Contact: Henry Benjamin, M.D., Director of Psychiatry, Northampton State Hospital, Room 351, Northampton, Massachusetts.

Dworin, Jack, Ph.D. (Tapes of 60 group psychotherapy sessions). Type of group: mixed adults and adolescents, all male at beginning, male and female mixed in later sessions. Setting: hospital. Type of treatment: eclectic intensive psychotherapeutic approach, predominantly neo-analytic. Contact: Jack Dworin, Ph.D., Director, Psychological Services, Torrance State Hospital, Torrance, Pennsylvania.

Kass, Leonard P. (Tapes of 3 parents' groups and 1 adult therapy group). Type treatment: supportive and nondirective. First sessions. Contact: Leonard P. Kass, Middlesex City Mental Health Clinic, 21 Remsen Avenue, New Brunswick, New Jersey.

Markenson, David, Ph.D., "Choice of Seating as Transference Phenomenon in Group Therapy." Type of group: female adults. Setting: outpatient clinic. Type of treatment: psychotherapeutic. Group members reflect how the places they chose to sit reflected their feelings toward one another, and therapist, and symbolize their needs. Contact: David Markenson, Ph.D., West Dade County Child Guidance Clinic, 1350 N.W. 14th Street, Miami, Florida.

Mullan, Hugh, M.D., "Therapeutic Moves in the Process of Group Psychotherapy." Three lectures presented before a mixed group of beginners at the 1961 Institute of the Southwestern Group Psychotherapy Society. Didactic presentation. Contact: Harold R. Winer, Ph.D., 8215 Westchester Drive, Dallas 25, Texas.

Roberts, Allyn F., Ph.D. (Tapes of 30 sessions). Types of groups: all males, all females, mixed sex, all psychotic, mixed psychotic and non-psychotic. Setting: hospital and outpatient clinic. Type of treatment: psychotherapeutic. Included are sessions with experienced and inexperienced group psychotherapists, beginning groups and groups which have been meeting for 1½ years, groups from lower socio-economic class backgrounds, and groups composed exclusively of professional persons. Contact: Allyn F. Roberts, Ph.D., Director, Psychology Department, Mendota State Hospital, 301 Troy Drive, Madison 4, Wisconsin.

Truax, Charles, Ph.D., "Initial Stages of Client-Centered Group Psychotherapy with Hospitalized Schizophrenics." Type of group: adult and late adolescent males. Setting: hospital. Type of treatment: active client-centered. Other tapes available. Contact: Charles B. Truax, Ph.D., Administrative Coordinator, Psychotherapy Research Section, University of Wisconsin, 1402 University Avenue, Madison 6, Wisconsin.

Walden, R. E., M.D., "Group Therapy with Severely Neurotic Out-Patients" (Tapes of 40 sessions). Type of group: male adult veterans with problems of passive-aggressivity. Setting: out-patient clinic. Type of treatment: analytically oriented psychotherapy. Helpful to those interested in seeing how an out-patient group works through some of their dependency strivings and the associated socio-economic dissatisfactions and begin to move toward a more satisfyingly actual life. Contact: R. R. Walden, M.D., Veterans Administration Hospital, Leech Farm Road, Pittsburgh 6, Pennsylvania.

These recordings may be secured by writing to the Audio-Visual Committee, American Group Psychotherapy Association, 1790 Broadway, New York, New York, or to the individuals listed above.

QUESTION: What is the function of supervision in a group psychotherapy program?

ANSWER: Supervision in group psychotherapy is as important as in any method of psychotherapy. The novelty of group psychotherapy does not mean that adequate supervision can be eliminated. Every effort should be made to secure adequate supervision.

Some "wild cat" group psychotherapists may have conveyed the idea that supervision is not necessary. Group psychotherapy is a professional discipline with a corpus of procedures based on accumulated experience. To neglect such experience in the practice of group psychotherapy is as dangerous as it would be in any other therapeutic endeavor.

Most important to any group psychotherapy program is adequate supervision of the personnel who are to do the actual treatment. Supervision may create a problem in some areas, as there may be few competent people available to act in this capacity. If the institution in which the program is to be initiated is located in an area where other sources of supervision may be obtained (other institutions or private practitioners), such persons may be contracted to assume this responsibility. If supervising personnel are not available in the immediate vicinity, it may be possible to have someone come in from a distance on a weekly or semimonthly basis. This supervision may be with each therapist individually or collectively on a group or workshop basis. Although the latter may not be the best technique of supervision, it has often been effective.

During supervisory sessions, both on-going cases and specific problems may be discussed. If it is not possible to obtain outside help, those who are involved in carrying out the group program may meet on a regular basis once or twice a week. The discussion of group sessions, either as a continuous case presentation or discussion of special problems, or both, by the total group, may offer help in resolving difficulties and act as a learning experience. The views and opinions of objective listeners who are not directly involved with the group may help to pick up and clarify disruptive influences like counter-transference factors operating in the group. Verbatim transcripts, tape recordings, and/or one-way screen observations may be invaluable aids for both supervision and learning.

In a small institution, the group therapy program may begin on the basis of a single group. In such a situation, the group therapist may discuss his goals and objectives with the intake personnel in relation to selection of patients. To facilitate beginning his first group, it may be advantageous for the therapist to start the group with patients whom he had been seeing previously in individual treatment. This procedure has the advantage of personal contact with and knowledge of each patient's psychodynamics. The therapist who already has developed a therapeutic relationship and a positive transference may make the shift from individual to group psychotherapy relatively easy.

As in institutional settings, it is often to the private practitioner's advantage to start his first group with patients who have been in individual treatment with him. The advantages of this procedure are that the therapist has a knowledge of the patient's psychodynamics as well as an established therapeutic relationship. Including his individual patients in the new group may eliminate future difficulties, as the therapist will already have an idea of the role and transference reactions each patient will have in the group.

There are occasions when the formation of a group from one's own individual patient load may have a boomerang effect. The group formation has a threatening effect on the homeostasis established between the therapist and patient. Inclusion of a patient from one's own individual case load may result in intense anxiety as the patient expresses a loss of exclusiveness with his therapist. There are times when the therapist, in his efforts to encourage an individual patient who has been in individual treatment for some time to enter a group, may stimulate the patient's fantasy where he may anticipate grandiose, unreal expectations. When these anticipated expectations are not immediately fulfilled upon entering the group, the patient may react with a feeling of intense hostility at having been "duped." As one patient expressed it, "You told me that coming into a group would increase my therapeutic progress. That's a laugh—the only thing that has happened in the month I've been here is that I've gotten into a hassle with almost everybody. This stuff is not for me—I don't like it, I don't want it, and I quit! I thought that coming into the group would show the progress I had made—instead, it's only creating more conflicts."

The private practitioner may increase his range of selection by including patients from other sources, i.e., patients of colleagues. The therapist may inform his colleagues that he is doing group psychotherapy. These other therapists may then refer patients who are no longer making progress in treatment or who may benefit from group psychotherapy for other reasons. The inclusion of other therapists' patients into a group may be as conjoint therapy, where the other therapists continue to see the patients on an individual basis.

There are also several other means which may be employed by the group therapist in obtaining patients for his groups. Group psychotherapy is relatively new as a therapeutic technique and many agencies as well as the general public are eager to learn and understand its potentials and advantages. The therapist may be asked by medical groups, hospital clinics, schools, civic organizations, and community social service agencies to lecture and discuss this psychotherapeutic method.

Legal Responsibilities

The legal responsibilities of the therapist in his practice of group psychotherapy can be discussed only on a broad basis. Psychotherapy and its definition and restrictions may vary from state to state within the United States as well as from country to country. An example of this is its use in the state of New York, where psychotherapy is a generic term on the statute books with no specific restrictions as to its practice. In some states, psychotherapy is part of the Medical Practices Act and its practice restricted to the physician. In consulting with different attorneys, no definitive clarification could be obtained. Not only does the law vary in different areas, but it is also so broad and allows for so many ramifications that anyone need only have sufficient funds to pay legal fees in order to bring legal action against a psychotherapist. No one can say, however, if the plaintiffs in such legal actions are likely to be successful in their action. If psychotherapy is under the Medical Practices Act and its practice restricted to physicians, anyone else who attempts to practice group psychotherapy is naturally committing an illegal act. Otherwise, the practice of group psychotherapy, as well as any other method of psychotherapy, may be considered as an effort on the part of the therapist to apply his talent and knowledge toward the most effective aid to his patient or client.

Group psychotherapy differs from individual psychotherapy in that it involves the bringing together of an interrelationship of several people. Within this context, there is always the possibility of acting out, which is not under the direct control of the therapist. Neither the group therapist, nor the individual therapist has complete control over the actions of his patients. Therefore, he can only do what he feels is most advantageous for each individual patient. If the patient, after entering treatment, becomes involved in an extramarital or other act which is disliked or undesired by a spouse or parent, the action is most likely a manifestation of the patient's problem rather than one created by the treatment procedure. In the case of minors, parents are not only aware of their child's being in treatment, but also usually consent to their being in a group.

A most important suggestion which may be offered is that the practitioner obtain malpractice insurance. This will alleviate unnecessary anxiety in the practitioner and minimizes the imposing of methods and/or restrictions which may be detrimental in the treatment. The therapist cannot prevent anyone's taking legal action even though there may be insufficient cause. Insurance companies which offer malpractice insurance are familiar with the "types" of people who tend to bring such legal actions and also are able to cope with the legal procedures much more effectively than the therapist. If the therapist is not protected by such insurance, he may be exposed to great financial loss, as well as loss of time, to prove that the accusations brought against him are not valid.

References

1. *Educational Film Guide*. New York, Wilson, 1960.
2. *Psychological Cinema Register*, Pa. State Univ.
3. NICHTENHAUSER, A., COLEMAN, M. L., and RUHE, D. S., *Films in Psychiatry, Psychology, and Mental Health*. New York, Health Education Council, 1953.
4. U. S. Office of Education. *A Directory of 3,300 16mm. Film Libraries*. Washington, Superintendent of Documents, 1957.

physical and other 4
arrangements

THE physical accoutrements of and the administrative arrangements for group therapy deserve a great deal more attention than they do in an individual therapy situation. In the individual situation, a desk and chair, and possibly a couch, represent relatively standard fixtures. Since the patient's primary activity is talking, he is not likely to use the physical dimensions of the therapeutic setting, except to comment on them from time to time. In the group situation it is possible that he may use the physical dimensions relatively actively. The dimensions include seating arrangements and the format of the therapy room. The administrative arrangements include time of day, length of session, taking notes, the use of observers, and fees. The therapist's employment of these dimensions should be a reflection of his own philosophy of and approach to treatment, as well as the special characteristics of each group of patients.

Seating Arrangement

Many group psychotherapists start a group by placing the chairs in the therapy room in a circle[1]. This has the advantage of permitting every member to see every other member and the therapist, and it reinforces the psychological significance of the circle. The circle is a concrete expression of the distance at which the members of a group will interact best without feeling overly remote or anxious. Shifting of chairs backward or forward can be observed when the "psychological space" among the group members is modified by group activity.

The sitting position of each member of the group may harden, with group members taking relatively fixed positions. The circle position may be threatening to some patients because they may resent or have difficulties in handling the closeness which the circle position communicates. Some therapists find it less threatening to the patients, especially in the initial stages of treatment, to have the chairs spread out along the wall of a rectangular or square room. These can be moved into a circular position as needed.

Where fixed and folding chairs are both available to patients, the patients requiring more emotional support from the group are likely to seek out the fixed chairs. The patients who are more independent or who wish to convey a feeling of being independent, tend to take a folding chair. Sofas are often avoided by neurotic patients because of their desire to avoid the closeness of someone sitting next to them.

Chairs may be selected by patients on the basis of their preference for a given kind of chair. Some prefer a straight and hard-backed chair because of sciatica or some back ailment, which makes a hard chair more comfortable. Some patients like to stretch out in a soft chair and put their feet on a stool, thus approaching a condition of relaxation almost akin to the patient fantasying while lying on a couch in individual psychoanalysis. Some therapists feel that it is desirable for the room to have an extra stool or ottoman, for the patient who feels like stretching out. For the differing needs of patients, it is a good idea to have a variety of kinds of chairs around the therapy room. Pregnant women or tall or stout persons are likely to prefer special chairs.

The chairs used for a group session may sometimes consist of whatever is available in the office or living room in which the therapist is functioning, so that he may not be able to select the chairs which he may want to have, at least initially. Some psychotherapists use their living room or the waiting room outside their regular office for group treatment in a private practice context, and are thus not likely to get completely new furniture specifically for their group therapy activity.

Patients often respond to the colors of the chairs in a therapy room, in accordance with how they feel on a particular day. The more expressively colored chairs may be selected by patients who have a need to express emotion. The duller-looking chairs may be selected by patients who feel less of a need to express emotion.

Few patients move their chairs during a therapy session. When they do, it is usually in response to their need to communicate something of importance about their reaction to the session. Some group members shift position in their chairs in order to express some feeling about the group or a particular group member, often the person sitting next to them.

When the group members wish to express anxiety, they often do so by moving their chairs close together, often into a circle. Any one group member may express anxiety by moving his chair away from the group. Anxiety is sometimes expressed by a patient going out of his way to sit on either side of the therapist. By doing so, the patient seems to derive symbolic strength from sitting near the therapist, who in such cases clearly represents some kind of parent-surrogate. The therapist's right often represents masculinity and his left often represents femininity.

Sitting on the floor and standing up may represent relatively unusual acting out behavior on the part of the patient in response to a given situation. A patient who consistently engages in such behavior is likely to be relatively disturbed, and the meaning of his atypical behavior should be of great concern to the therapist. Sitting near the door may be one way in which a patient expresses his alienation from the group and his desire to leave it. Patients with a need to avoid contact may move their chairs out of the group.

Anxiety may be more connected with some chairs than with others for some patients because of special associations which such chairs have. When the therapist sees some patients individually as well as in a group, as in combined treatment, the chair in which he sits during individual sessions may have special connotations, often of anxiety, to patients who see this chair as part of the setting for group therapy. The therapist may wish to sit in his own chair because it is the one in which he feels most comfortable, and because he has to sit all day whereas patients come for an hour or two. Some therapists have no preferred chair and sit in any chair.

Most therapists find that keeping their chairs on the same level as that of the patient, rather than setting them apart in some way, facilitates the group interaction. There are some therapists who prefer to keep their chairs apart in such a way that they stand out from those of the patients, so that the position of the chair symbolizes their leadership role.

Sometimes the patients will use seating arrangements in order to establish themselves into two or more subgroups. These groups may be a continuation of subgroups which emerged at a previous session, or at some informal warm-up activity in the waiting room or elsewhere prior to the commencement of the session itself. The therapist may utilize these subgroups in his treatment activity by calling attention to them and assisting the members to understand their significance.

The Room

The room in which group therapy takes place may have an effect on the group members[2]. The smaller the room the more intimate the group feeling may be. The larger the room, the more likely is it that some detached patients will feel free to express their alienation. The room's color may have effects on the group. A small room has the disadvantage of possibly becoming heavy with smoke fumes if there are a number of smokers in a group in which smoking is permitted. Some patients will be uncomfortable and get red eyes from such a small room. It is thus extremely important that there be adequate ventilating equipment in a small room.

Adequate ashtrays are important in a therapy room where smoking is permitted. They may be of the floor variety, as a precautionary measure, because experience has shown that the small table ashtray is likely to be the first object in sight when a patient has an impulse to throw something at another group member. If table ashtrays are used, they might be preferably of the bean bag variety, because if they are thrown, the relatively soft bean bags are likely to hit the target first.

Facial tissues can be available throughout the room. There will be patients who will wish to cry or blow their noses or use the tissue for some such purpose. Its being clearly visible and available can eliminate panic-arousing anxiety for some patients. It is desirable that there be a bathroom available not only for the patients but also accessible to persons in the waiting room.

The therapy room is likely to provide a number of cues which may be detected by patients. They may, for example, comment on paintings which may be on display. Some patients may say that they do not like a painting in the room when they wish to express negative feelings about the therapist or other members of the group. Others may gain symbolic support by looking at a painting in the room, when they feel under attack by group members. Looking at a painting may make it easier for a patient to express withdrawal from a group, because the painting may be perceived as a nonthreatening inanimate object. The therapist can be sensitized to this kind of communication in a group. Other physical features of a room may lead to similar comments.

In general, it is often desirable that there be a number of lamps throughout the therapy room. This may permit the members of the group to modify the lighting arrangements in the room in a way which is responsive to their needs and which may provide a dimension of communication which may be of possible therapeutic use by the therapist and the group. Eye and face movements which may be significant may be visible[3].

The accoustics of the therapy room would ideally minimize noise from other offices or from the street. Patients tend to seize on such noise and express negative feelings about it when they have free-floating anxiety or aggressiveness. The noise provides a vehicle for the expression of the anxiety or aggression. Some group therapists have found that introducing music for special purposes into group sessions may be useful. Where there is great resistance, and playing a carefully selected record has occasionally been successfully used in loosening up the group.

Rugs on the floor are usually desirable. They not only soften and absorb sound but tend to reinforce the feeling of closeness of the group. Rugs may subtly help to confirm the responsibility of not discussing group activities with the outside world, which the patients often are required to assume. Since many of the matters discussed in group therapy are disagreeable, the rug seems to have a more psychologically soothing effect on patients than does an ordinary uncovered wood floor. If the therapy occurs under circumstances in which a rug is not available, then the therapist should, of course, do the best he can with available facilities.

If one group session follows directly after another, it is necessary that the therapist give some thought to the room which will hold those waiting for the next session. This can be a much more serious problem with a group than is the case in individual therapy. A group, because of the special momentum of a particular session or because of some therapeutic contingency which cannot be anticipated, may run over the expected time. Since there are always patients who come early, a considerable number of patients may therefore be milling around unless some specific provision is made for them. Such provisions should include not only a place where they can sit down, but also a place where they can put coats, packages, umbrellas, and other impediments which they may have. The encounter of the members of the group which is leaving by the members of the next group may be difficult for some members, especially in private treatment, and any procedures which maximize discretion in arrivals and departures on the part of members of the groups are desirable.

It is wise for the therapist to allow up to perhaps a half hour between the end of one group and the beginning of the next. This will not only minimize encounters between groups but will enable the therapist to prepare adequately for the next session. A patient may remain behind when the rest of the group leaves because he has had an anxiety attack, and the therapist has the responsibility for helping such casualties.

Time of Day of Session

It is possible that the time of day at which a group session occurs may have some "rub-off" on the content and direction of the session. In an institutional setting, the time of the session is likely to be somewhat less relevant to the patient than is the case with group members who have to find time for treatment out of their daily routine.

Groups which meet just before a traditional mealtime are often likely to express aggressiveness which is related to their hunger. If they meet just after a traditional mealtime, they may be somewhat less active than a group which meets at other times. Associations to eating are more likely to be found in groups which meet around a mealtime than if they meet at some other time.

A group which meets at the end of the day, when its members are tired, might be expected to be more relaxed and thus to have fewer defensive reactions than might otherwise be the case. What often happens is that the members' fatigue translates itself into relative withdrawal. The presence of other members makes it relatively easier for any one group member not to participate because of fatigue than would be the case in individual treatment. The fatigue may be real or it may be a defense, and the therapist should attempt to establish the nature of the fatigue. At group sessions which are conducted at all hours, there are likely to be some people who say they are tired.

One time which offers special difficulties is lunchtime, when some office workers seek to arrange their group therapy sessions. The worker is likely to be concerned about his transportation to and from the scene of the therapy. He may be worried about what will face him when he gets back to work, and have difficulty in disengaging himself from the ongoing flow of his work in order to enter into the special demands of the group therapy situation.

Length of Session

Like all other external modalities of group treatment, the length of the session is a function of a variety of different factors. These include the larger goals of the group, how often it meets, and the level of treatment which the therapist finds appropriate. In general, a group which meets more than once a week can productively have shorter periods for each meeting than a group which meets only once a week.

Even with a group which meets several times a week, a period of one full hour has been found to be almost minimally necessary in order to permit the group process to unfold itself. It has been found that groups which meet for more than two and a half hours are likely to be retracing their activities and to reach a point of diminishing returns in terms of optimum utilization of time.

The level of the group therapy will be related to the therapist's decision on how long the group session should optimally be. If a therapist practices psychoanalytic group therapy with dreams and unconscious material part of the regular content of group sessions, it is unlikely that a one-hour period would permit adequate ventilation of such material. One hour might, however, be an ideal length for a guidance group. The decision on length of treatment should be a reflection of the therapist's general approach to his work rather than a separate decision.

Taking Notes, Recording and Observers

Some psychotherapists take notes on the progress of their groups and some do not. Beginning group psychotherapists often find it desirable to take notes because there may be a considerable number of participants who may make contributions to any given meeting of a group. They may feel that it is helpful to make notes in order to help themselves in summing up what a group has done and as a useful review prior to the next meeting of the group. For evaluation purposes in which a group psychotherapist is being supervised, some record of the group session may be constructively used.

No notes taken after a group meeting have the detail and immediacy of those which are taken during a session. The need to be alert to the activity taking place within the group makes it all but impossible for the therapist to take the kind of notes during the session which are often relatively easy for the individual therapist to take. Many therapists find that they can take adequate notes if they allow ten or fifteen minutes right after a session for this purpose.

Notes on a session might cover the themes of the session, any members who appeared to be especially active or inactive, interrelationships among the group members, transference phenomena, dreams, continuation of discussions from previous sessions, the introduction of new material, the therapist's reactions, or anything else which the therapist may regard as worthy of record for future reference.

Some therapists have used tape or other recording devices for keeping some kind of record of group sessions. One of the disadvantages of the recording of a therapy session is that it takes an hour to listen to each hour that is recorded. Therapists who start tape-recorded sessions often underestimate the time involved in listening to the recordings. If time is available for listening to records of group meetings, then they may certainly be used for a wide variety of functions. Of course a group should be told of any arrangements for recording a session and shown the location of the recording equipment. The initial reaction of the group members is likely to be one of concern about being recorded, but this generally evaporates after the first ten or fifteen minutes. Patients usually forget that the recording device is on and ignore it once they get into the session.

Some settings which have one-way mirrors make it relatively easy for an observer to observe a group. There are situations when therapists have occasion for an observer to sit in on a group. The observer may be a student therapist, a professional from another discipline, an administrator, or some other person who is not a patient or a potential patient for this group. The introduction of a new person who is not on the level of the patients can be potentially frightening to the group because of their feeling that the stranger will be privy to and possibly judge their private thoughts. Ideally, the therapist should ask the group's permission before introducing an observer, and candidly explain the purpose of the observer's presence. It is better to err in the direction of telling a group too much rather than too little about the role of an observer in advance of the visit. A therapist in an institutional setting has much more latitude in inviting observers than would a private practitioner.

An observer who is a regular member of a group can be an invaluable aid to the group therapist. It is possible that he can be useful to the therapist in maintaining a record of the sessions. The observer, even if he says nothing, is likely to be the object of some of the group's transference relationships. This role of the observer may be both useful and sometimes difficult for the therapist. The observer's silence is likely to be perceived by the patients as being judgmental and they may resent it. They may think that the observer is evaluating the therapist as well as the patients.

A more formal procedure for keeping records of group sessions is through a group secretary. She is usually a stenographer who is not a patient, who sits inside or perhaps just outside the line of vision of the group. She can keep a record of the threads that run through the session, make notes on everything that is said, or any point in between these extremes which the therapist may find useful. Patients usually react negatively to the idea of a stranger who is a nonparticipant taking notes, but they are likely to change their attitudes after they realize that the secretary is not threatening. Some group therapists use a group secretary's summary of what happened at the last session as the introduction to the next session. They often find that, especially with groups which meet relatively infrequently, hearing a summary of a group's last meeting helps the patients to remember reactions to the previous meeting and thus maintain some connection with what has happened before.

Persons who are new to group psychotherapy are sometimes startled to see a group which may have two observers and a continuing tape recording being made of its activities, and which is being studied through a one-way mirror. They are startled because the activities of the group appear to be proceeding without regard for the presence of the observers, the recording machine or the mirror. Group members usually get so engrossed in what they are doing that they take little cognizance of anything else.

Fees

Fees may represent a source of resistance on the part of the patient who is required to pay them. In institutional or clinical settings, where there is no fee, there can be no problem unless the patient feels he should pay. The therapist can then help the patient to understand why he thinks he should pay when there is no fee. In some settings, where the patient pays a standard fee to a cashier or some other third person, it is important for the therapist to be kept informed of whether the patient pays his fee and to deal with nonpayment appropriately. The therapist does not abrogate his responsibility for the fee merely because he does not collect it personally.

In any kind of setting it is necessary to recognize that discussing money and fees may occasion conflicts in both therapist and group members. Some group members find it much easier to discuss sex than to discuss money. Where there are difficulties about fees, full consideration should be given to the real as well as the symbolic importance of the problem.

The therapist in private practice is likely to have difficulties in handling fees primarily if he does not make explicit the amount of the fee and the mechanics of how it should be paid. If different rates are charged various patients, friction may arise as a result of patients' discovering what the other patients pay. The therapist should accept his inability to keep the patients from discovering what the others pay. They find out ultimately, and it is unseemly for the therapist to appear to be doing something underhanded by pledging patients to secrecy about fees. Problems about fees should be ventilated during the group sessions. If patients are supposed to pay and do not do so, this should be discussed as part of treatment.

One occasion for fee difficulty is that patients in private practice sometimes believe that the therapist should not get any more from the combined fees of a group than he should get from an individual patient for the same time. For example, a patient may pay $5.00 an hour for group treatment. If he sees that there are six members in the group, he may assume that they are all paying $5.00 and that the therapist thus is getting $30.00 for roughly the same amount of time for which he used to get $15.00 for an individual session. The patient may ask the group therapist for an explanation of why "your rates have gone up so quickly."

Some therapists have told the group that they want, let us say, $35.00 from the group for the session, and then leave it to the group to assess each of its members "democratically." Such procedures almost never work out because it is too big a responsibility for the patients to carry. The patients seem to feel that it is a proper function for a therapist to decide and collect fees, but not a function which patients should handle.

Each of these external modalities of group treatment may not appear to be important by itself. Each one, however, contributes toward the atmosphere within which therapy occurs and the total impact of all of these dimensions may be considerable.

References

1. WINICK, C., and HOLT, H., Seating position as non-verbal communication in group analysis. *Psychiatry 24*:171, 1961.
2. WINICK, C., and HOLT, H., Some external modalities of group psychotherapy and their dynamic significance. *Am. J. Psychotherapy 15*:56, 1961.
3. WINICK, C., and HOLT, H., Eye and face movements as non-verbal communication in group psychotherapy. *J. Hillside Hospital, 11*:67, 1962.

selection of patients for 5
group psychotherapy

IN ADDITION to physical and administrative arrangements, several key questions must be faced before any group therapy program can be launched. What is the background and training of people who will take over these groups? What types of patients are immediately available? What types of patients will be available to replenish the first group or to form later ones?

It is necessary to decide on the kind of group which will best serve each type of patient in a particular setting. The kind of approach that may be especially desirable for a guidance clinic is likely to be inappropriate for a psychotic ward. In addition to the approach of the group therapist, another dimension to be considered is the purpose of the group itself.

Different aspects of therapy are stressed in different types of groups. Reality problems of the here-and-now are paramount in guidance and counseling groups; the interaction process is emphasized in relationship groups; and reconstructive therapy is the goal of analytic groups. The therapist's role and his selection of patients will depend upon how he perceives group therapy in general, and what goals he hopes to achieve for his group.

Intake Procedures

The intake department is of the utmost importance in organizing new groups in institutional settings, and in maintaining a reservoir from which patients may be selected for groups already under way. In large institutions one member of the department may be designated as the intake group psychotherapist charged with following through on procedures which aid in placing patients in the appropriate therapy group. The intake staff will need to have continuous liaison with the administrator of the group program. In this way all concerned will be aware of the current case load; the age, sex, and diagnosis of patients on the waiting list; and community needs that have not yet been met by the institution. The administrator and all intake personnel should review diagnostic criteria for referrals and discuss how to prepare patients to accept group therapy.

In his initial interview the intake psychotherapist should make clear to the patient that the staff will decide whether individual or group treatment would be more helpful or whether a combination of the two forms of treatment would be even more helpful. His possible puzzlement or reluctance to accept a recommendation for group therapy may sometimes be partially alleviated by offering appropriate literature describing group therapy[1] and citing its advantages. A leaflet or other brief statement can be prepared to fit the needs of a particular institution. But even if such an explanation is available it is important for the intake person to cope with the patient's uncertainty and anxiety. It is suggested that the patient—before being placed in therapy—join a special orientation or intake group, if available. Here many of his questions will be aired and clarified.

What Are Intake Groups?

In institutional or outpatient clinics, intake groups—also known as vestibule, diagnostic, holding, or orientation groups—provide a preliminary group experience for patients awaiting a specific assignment or referral for psychotherapy[2]. Even though brief, this experience is potentially rewarding. It may relieve the patient's initial anxieties and clarify his impressions of therapy, as well as give him basic information that will facilitate the first phase of treatment and prepare him for further psychotherapy. The intake group provides one means of evaluating the patient's needs and maintaining contact with him until he is referred elsewhere.

A trained group psychotherapist or group case worker who observes ten to twenty patients while they air anxieties, fears, resistances, and distortions in free discussion can gain a good impression of their personality structures. This knowledge will aid him in selecting a type of treatment that will benefit each, and in setting up specific groups or individual treatment with specific therapists.

Commercial films and mental health films, with a central theme such as the difficulties of growing up or sibling rivalry, are often shown and discussed in relation to the patients' life experiences. Some therapists using this technique show only excerpts from the films and encourage group members to supply the denouement. Each patient's version may be helpful to himself and to the other members and the therapist since it will reflect certain of his problems and reveal the patterns of his perceptions and distortions of life. When patients recognize the part played by anxieties and defenses, via their identification with characters and situations in the films, they often find it easier to start coping with their own resistances and to reinforce each other's motivation for psychotherapy.

Like more formal psychotherapy groups, intake groups either have changing membership (open) or have relatively constant membership (closed). In a closed group, ten to twenty patients may meet for ten to fifteen weekly sessions of one to one-and-a-half hours. Intake groups often tend to be open because of the rapidly changing patient population in a hospital, clinic or social service setting. These groups have included as many as fifty patients.

The intake group may foster a considerable degree of self-understanding[3]. In some instances sessions are also open to relatives of the patients and to others in the community. To emphasize the professional nature of this service, it may be advantageous to charge a nominal fee, either by the session or by the month. The fee becomes symbolic of the professional help received.

Characteristics of Intake Groups

Therapists should be alert to the possible anxiety contagion in an intake group. If such anxiety is not dealt with promptly, either in the group or in individual consultations, some patients are likely to become so overwhelmed that they will drop out.

A man in a closed intake group at an outpatient clinic said, "A colleague of mine committed suicide after he'd been in psychotherapy for some time. Lots of people felt that if he hadn't been in treatment he'd be alive today." After a few moments' silence a number of other patients brought out stories—some highly colored, some second- or third-hand—of persons who had deserted their families, become divorced, or "cracked up" while in therapy. The co-therapist, in an effort to discharge the mounting anxiety contagion said jokingly, "I was in analysis and my life wasn't disrupted." The therapist, realizing that the anxiety was still very acute, said, "My great-grandparents, my grandparents, my parents, and several friends have died in bed, and all from different diseases. Do you think it's safe for me to go to bed tonight?" Although laughter released some tension the anxiety contagion caused the members to gather around the therapist at the close of the session. The tenor of their questions was: "Will therapy really help us? At least, can you guarantee that we won't be worse afterward? Can we see you alone? How long will we have to wait to get in a regular group?"

Rapid establishment of transference to the therapist and close rapport among the members in intake groups of ten to fifteen may make the patients reluctant to be reassigned when the waiting period is over. Indeed, some intake groups have continued virtually intact as therapy groups, accepting the therapist's decision to transfer one or two patients to other groups better suited to their needs. In intake groups of fifteen to fifty, where their ties to the therapist and to peers are not likely to be as close, patients are more willing to separate and face a new situation when the waiting period is over.

Criteria for Selection

A number of different criteria have been successful in selecting patients for group psychotherapy. Diverse opinions have been reviewed, among them Slavson's approach[4]. He has suggested four general criteria: The patient should have experienced "minimal satisfaction in his primary relations some time during his childhood"; he should be subject to a minimal degree of sexual disturbance; he should possess basic ego sufficiency and "a minimal super-ego development."

He cites two types of contraindications, one set derived from inherent problems of patients and the other from the effect patients may have on each other and on the group. Slavson excludes persons who show inadequacy in primary relations, and also regards intense sexual disturbances, regressive infantile character, and extreme narcissism as contraindications to group treatment.

In contrast, Freedman and Sweet[5] believe the group situation tends to avert danger for the patient with enfeebled reality ties, possibly preventing premature engulfment by unconscious material which his ego is not yet equipped to handle. Three nosological categories are recommended for inclusion in group treatment: (1) patients for whom inflexible social roles serve as a defense against anxiety; (2) those who cannot countenance any form of dependency; (3) those who are likely to evoke negative counter-transference reactions because of their belligerent demands and exceptionally coercive tactics. Freedman and Sweet and others have found group therapy the method of choice for a number of their "sickest" patients, with individual therapy reserved for psychoneurotics.

Other therapists advocate a less extreme approach. Leopold[6] suggests that patients selected for psychotherapy in groups should have:

(1) Full reality contact. Those who constantly interject their irrational productions cannot be reached by other members.

(2) The capacity for being reached emotionally in an interpersonal relationship. Persons who monopolize the group over a protracted period block all interaction.

(3) Sufficient flexibility to increase or reduce intragroup tensions. Patients unable to cope with their own or others' anxiety-provoking unconscious productions become a burden to the group.

(4) The ability to act as a catalyst from time to time. Patients whose behavior is destructive, impulse-ridden or antisocial arouse realistic fears in other members.

There also has been a considerable trend away from strictly formal diagnostic criteria toward what may be called experiential procedures. A therapist who uses the experiential method does not make formal or separate diagnoses of each patient before placing him into a group. He places a patient in a group on the basis of his clinical impression. The patient sometimes remains or is later transferred.

The group therapist's principal concern is to place patients in the group climate best meeting their particular needs. For example, the question of whether a patient with low ego strength is suitable for group therapy cannot be answered by a simple yes or no. Either reply is likely to be inaccurate and misleading, because the main determinant is the interaction between patients with different diagnostic criteria, and the group's blending of the resulting elements. Clinical diagnoses such as borderline or paranoid schizophrenia, character disorder, anxiety neurosis, and anxiety hysteria are much more meaningful when considered with the individual's psychodynamics. The patient's diagnosis may even sometimes be less meaningful than his psychodynamics in group interaction.

Regardless of formal criteria of selection or the therapist's philosophy, he must recognize several parameters when considering patients for a particular group:

(1) *Index-of-anxiety reaction.* How will the patient cope with the added tension caused by entering a group? How will the group cope with the added tension caused by a newcomer? What familial and familiar reactions will be elicited in him and in others? Will he or other members be "thrown" by such anxieties?

(2) *Identification and empathy with others.* Does any other group member have similar problems or symptoms? Does he have a similar background or similar life experience? Will any group members be able to empathize with the new patient's problems? Will the new patient be able to empathize with other members in the group?

(3) *Ego strength.* How vulnerable are the patient's ego processes to interpersonal stress? Is he able to withstand attack from a member of the group? Is he able to permit closeness with other members?

(4) *Interlocking of patients' defense systems.* How will each group member's defensive system react with that of the new member? What will be the effect of any interlocking that may occur? Will the patient react with denial or internalize? Will he become involved in destructive acting out?

Anthony[7] has called attention to the dovetailing of diagnostic categories and to patients' seesawing between them, each state provoking and eliciting various reactions. The therapist who views patients with various types of pathology in relation to each other tends to rely less and less on absolute categories, more and more on their interrelationships and interactions. The Menninger Clinic, America's largest psychiatric training center, has practically abandoned diagnostic categories. The significance of such categories steadily recedes as the group is viewed in its totality. Though each member is an entity, he is seen not in isolation but acting and interacting with other members whose disturbances may be similar to his own or entirely different.

According to Anthony[7] group therapy liberated him from the tendency to freeze people into diagnostic categories: "I began to see diagnosis, interdiagnosis, and then group diagnosis in action." In addition to the instinctual and defensive reactions elicited in all group therapy sessions he recognized what he called complementary transactions, which are of six types: exhibitionistic-voyeuristic; heterosexual-homosexual; sadistic-masochistic; penis pride-penis envy; manic-depressive, and progression-regression.

Selection in Institutional and Outpatient Settings

The selection of patients for a psychotherapy group within a mental hospital poses special problems. As many as four fifths of the inmates of such a hospital may be divided into three main groups:
(1) Patients hospitalized for an extended period;
(2) Patients recently admitted in an acutely disturbed state;
(3) "Revolving door" patients, so called because they are constantly in and out as the result of repeated acute crises. They may also be described in terms of regression, psychomotor disturbances, severe acting out, withdrawn and ideational disturbances.

Emphasis in hospital treatment may be directed in several ways, *e.g.*, toward remotivation of autistic patients, problems with closed-ward patients, combined treatment with patients not threatened by one-to-one relationships, or homogeneous groups (patients suffering from the same disease, insulin shock patients, senile patients, etc.). All groups must begin to cope with their current problems. Treatment with limited goals has been successfully undertaken by appropriately trained attendants or nurses under the supervision of group therapists. Institutional restraints tend to guard against serious acting out, and issues of war behavior become salient.

The day hospital is a new kind of quasi-institutional setting which provides added opportunities for the application of group psychotherapy. A related development in after-care facilities is the open-door policy of some hospitals. Because of the growing popularity of these developments, in which group therapy is the treatment of choice, the therapist must consider a number of elements in the social context of the patient's life situation:

(*1*) Does the patient live virtually in social isolation in the community, or does he have a nuclear family? If residing with his own family, does the head of the household work?

(*2*) Does he live with an acquired family? If so, is the spouse working? Is he cared for by someone other than the spouse?

(*3*) How well do persons in his immediate environment tolerate his deviance? Are his relatives eager for him to receive outpatient treatment, or do they prefer that he be institutionalized?

The revolution in the treatment of emotional disorders, culminating in the open-door policy of hospitals, has paralleled the growth of group therapy. Day hospitals offering group therapy have reported improvement of 70 to 80 per cent of their patients, including some who were previously considered untreatable.

After-care departments of mental hospitals may wish to focus on various types of group treatment. In deciding which procedure is suitable for a patient, it will be helpful to keep in mind the following: (*1*) discussion groups; (*2*) social clubs; (*3*) group counseling or guidance; (*4*) analytic group psychotherapy; (*5*) combined treatment; (*6*) couple groups; and (*7*) treatment in family groups. The same alternatives may be relevant for outpatient clinics and private practice.

Placement in a Homogeneous or Heterogeneous Group [8, 9]

Intake personnel are charged with deciding whether a given patient is likely to do better in a homogeneous group where the other patients' diagnoses or symptomatology are similar, or in a heterogeneous group where these factors may be very dissimilar. A homogeneous group can be described only by using diagnostic labels inasmuch as there is no absolute homogeneity in any group, because of the patients' different individual psychodynamics, social status, cultural and economic backgrounds, interests, race, religion, and education. In a heterogeneous group these very differences generate tension and friction. However, the stimulation of contrasting personalities, pathologies, and problems tends to facilitate group movement.

It is in general therapeutically desirable to combine patients with a wide range of educational levels and occupations as well as varying degrees of sophistication. Communication may be facilitated by a patient with little formal education who insists on keeping the language at a level understandable to all. "I don't get those fancy expressions," said one housewife patient in a group made up largely of professional people. "Tell me in simple words how you felt, what you said and did. . . ."

Of course, a certain level of intelligence is essential in order for members to communicate with each other to some degree and to follow each other's thought processes. One group with an excellent climate for interaction included a college professor, father of three; a a housewife with two children; a married teacher who was childless; an unmarried artist; a housewife from the lower socio-economic stratum; an unmarried laborer; a married contractor with two children. The age range was from the early thirties to the late forties. There was wide variation in economic status, jobs and professions, religious and cultural backgrounds.

Experience suggests that a 20-year age gap is feasible when all group members are over 20. But young adults who have not had any sexual experience should probably not be placed in a group with people whose sexual experience has been extensive. This contact may pose difficulties for late adolescents and young adults, especially those from a strict religious and moralistic background. Their conflicts often become so unbearable that they may destructively act out or even leave the group.

It may be wise to avoid placing older persons, particularly women over 60 whose lives are lonely and isolated, in a group where the other members have active relationships of some kind. The resulting hostile parental transference tends to make the older members even more frustrated and aware of a void in their lives.

Patients who may arouse considerable fear, guilt, pity, and hostility reactions are better placed in a homogeneous group. Among patients in this category are alcoholics, acute psychotics, drug addicts, epileptics, psychopathic personalities, stutterers, patients suffering from ulcers, palsy, or aphasia. In a mixed group an alcoholic, drug addict, or even an ulcer patient may be the target of accusations: "You just need to lay off the stuff and you'll be all right." . . . "Don't expect us to help you when you're still hitting the bottle." . . . "Stop worrying and stick to your diet and you'll get over your ulcer." . . . "We've got problems of our own and don't want to waste all our time on you when you won't do anything to help yourself." Lack of empathy, particularly early in treatment, is very discouraging and threatening. The therapist will have to help the group members become more tolerant of each other's symptoms, which—regardless of the diagnosis—are equally distressing to each of them.

Patients with psychosomatic complaints evidenced by such conditions as serious skin disorders, ulcers, or allergic reactions may be placed in either homogeneous or heterogeneous groups. If their condition is not likely to provoke extreme reactions in other members, they may well benefit, and be benefited by, a heterogeneous group.

Since the psychosomatic patient often suffers openly, he is unlikely to be resistant in early group therapy sessions. He demands acceptance because of his need for immediate help. For example, a patient who suffered from severe migraine headaches listened to the discussion for half an hour during the first session and then said, "You people have lots of time to talk and talk. I haven't worked for eight days because of my headache. No pills relieve me any more. I want you to help me get rid of it."

Many therapy groups start with three to eight members and in agency settings the number may be twelve to fifteen, providing for a certain number of drop-outs. However, five is a good number with which to begin. When this nuclear unit becomes established, with both the therapist and members feeling secure, a few other patients may be admitted to help fulfill the specific needs of the group. Whether in private practice, in a clinic, agency, or institution, it is advisable for the therapist to start a group with the number with which he feels most comfortable. Sometimes it is the number representing his own nuclear family.

There is little doubt that the nosological classifications and psychodynamic structures of patients vary more widely in clinics and institutions than in private practice—a fact facilitating the group selection process. It must be reiterated that the therapist's main concern in selecting patients for treatment is: Will this particular patient help or interfere with communication in this particular group?

Mixed Groups: Psychotics and Neurotics

Group therapists have discussed at length the effect of introducing psychotics, borderline schizophrenics and patients with character disorders into a group of psychoneurotics.

With very few exceptions, patients with long-standing psychoses— whose ego is already overburdened by the invasion of autistic thoughts —find it difficult to follow the rapid shift of communication, both verbal and nonverbal, in analytic group psychotherapy. Unlike borderline schizophrenics, they have little capacity for identifying with other group members. Thus the presence of overtly psychotic patients leads other group members to ward off their own fugitive fantasies and to shore up their own defenses. However, in a well-integrated group, the individual attributes of such a psychotic member may prove compensatory or even in some way rewarding for the group as well as for himself.

A man in his middle twenties with a diagnosis of paranoid schizophrenia, who had lost six months of individual treatment, was placed in an analytic psychotherapy group that had functioned well for three years. He was a brilliant musician and seemed headed for a concert career. He spoke several languages well, was handsome and witty. He habitually sat on the floor near the therapist and rarely spoke. Even after a year he did not know the names of all the group members. But at times he responded with a fantasy couched in musical terms or with an extraordinarily pertinent and clever remark which provoked laughter and loosened tensions. Because of these occasional contributions the group valued and supported him.

Some borderline or latent schizophrenic patients function on what appears to be a neurotic level. They may be especially productive in analyzing dreams and tend to become excellent "adjunct therapists." For these patients analytic groups may well be the therapy of choice.

For other borderline schizophrenics characterized by emotional deprivation and a sense of isolation, the climate of a heterogeneous group seems to attenuate the threat of too much closeness. They can establish identification with peers which is less threatening to them than identification with authority figures. They are able to be in and out of the group, both literally and figuratively, moving at their own pace and discretion. They may even fall asleep if the tension becomes too great for them. In this group setting such patients can test the effectiveness of their defenses in protracted interpersonal contact with other members. In a homogeneous group they may not have sufficient opportunity to correct interpersonal relationships, because of their tendency to withdraw and expect too much from the therapist and from each other.

Some experts in the field feel strongly that ambulatory schizophrenics can be successfully treated in mixed analytic groups, although they must be protected early in the group therapeutic process. Since they have brittle personalities they may drop out of treatment if forced prematurely to face anxiety-provoking material. On the other hand, a good percentage of these patients—especially the hostile, aloof, and "righteous" type—often provoke a great deal of hostility. In groups where many members are afraid to launch a direct attack on their real target, the therapist, they use such a patient as a scapegoat. The therapist who understands this deflection of hostility can protect the frightened schizophrenic by offering himself as a target. Hulse[10] found that the majority of patients responded well, and showed fewer depressive and fearful feelings, greater closeness to reality, more social activity and responsibility, and improved social relations, as well as contributing to the treatment of neurotic group members. He differentiates between the large number of schizophrenics who are definitely psychotic and the smaller number who are not psychotic but definitely ill. An in-between category includes patients who are prepsychotic or in remission from a psychotic episode (the remission having occurred naturally or through ataraxic drugs, electroshock, or insulin shock). He feels that patients suffering from the so-called pseudoneurotic schizophrenias and borderline states can be treated in mixed analytic groups, but stresses that diagnosis of the "in-betweens" is very difficult.

Wolman has cited the advantages of group therapy for most types of latent schizophrenics[11]. Among the exceptions are patients who cannot tolerate the group, presumably because they have previously been too hurt in social relations to incur further risks on this score; and patients whom the group cannot tolerate because of their consistent acting out, which may include threatening other members and forcing them to drop out.

Wolman and others recommend treating obsessional and manic-depressive patients together, and Wolman would include psychopathic personalities. He believes their "careless manners," assertiveness and lack of scruples may further their own therapeutic progress. In general, psychopathic personalities—like adolescents—seem to work best in groups where the therapist maintains a highly authoritative role. Because of their brittle ego control, both require an authority figure to support them in their respective relationships. Neither group superego nor incentive provided by the group exerts a sufficient regulatory influence on these patients.

Wolman believes that the characteristic blandness of the latent schizophrenic tends to impress manic-depressive patients and may make him sympathetic to them. Manic-depressives—talkative, self-assured, sometimes tactless—may discover that their elation is not a sign of power, or their depression a sign of weakness.

Character Disorders

Group therapy may be the treatment of choice for some patients with character disorders, especially during the initial phase of therapy. They are likely to need a long time to face their own conflicts while maintaining their facade. They tend to take flight from their own anxieties and continually seek security by identifying with others. They often act as peacemakers and are well suited for this role because of their keen perceptions and ability to identify readily. Some are also easily drawn into the role of antagonist-provocateur in the group where their overpowering defenses and resistances may diminish, thus preparing the way for later individual treatment.

Classified under the many types of character disorders are narcissistic, passive-dependent, and passive-aggressive personalities. They cannot be expected to form meaningful relationships and function solely with group support. Their primitive ego structure, together with their often socially adequate defenses, is likely to call for a prolonged period of combined treatment. Such patients seem to progress best in treatment if the therapist encourages a continuing positive transference. This can be facilitated by letting the group members tackle the patient's defenses and egocentricity, rather than doing this himself, to help him overcome his infantile behavior and insatiable hunger for acceptance and love. He will continue to seek evidence of the therapist's acceptance and love.

Social Deviants

Social deviants like homosexuals, exhibitionists, voyeurs and others traditionally classified as perverts, seem to be more threatening to many a therapist than to other group members. This is especially true of therapists who are overprotective and overanxious toward their group members. The homosexual has proved to be particularly valuable in a heterogeneous group. He readily elicits both conscious and unconscious psychosexual conflicts so that members previously unable even to voice similar conflicts may follow his lead.

There is no question that the presence of a social deviant in a group presents certain problems. However, the therapist's acceptance of this patient may enable other members to bring out socially unacceptable events and fantasies in their lives with less fear of losing the therapist's approval[12]. The group is an open forum in which the uncovering process goes on constantly. In this setting each group member is helped to show himself in his nakedness—a process allowing him to see other members in their nakedness. The therapist may assume that these mutual disclosures will take place whether or not the group includes one or more social deviants.

The exhibitionist is apt to arouse hostile feelings, particularly from mothers in the group. Frustrated by his exhibitionistic drives, he may require a prolonged one-to-one relationship before entering the group. The voyeur is also a doubtful prospect for group psychotherapy inasmuch as he may receive gratifications, fostering his neurosis in the group situation.

The therapist must be wary about placing in a group patients who may encourage antisocial behavior, since he must assume full responsibility for exposing the members to possible physical assault. Patients whose behavior is definitely antisocial usually need a structured setting like that imposed by an institution. However, some therapists report success with this type of patient in private practice and outpatient settings.

Criteria of Selection for Children's Psychotherapy

Special criteria are needed in selecting children for group treatment[13]. Groups are usually homogeneous with respect to age and sex and smaller than adult groups. It is generally agreed that grouping by age is very important since certain treatment modalities are especially appropriate for each age range. Play therapy is used for nursery children and activity therapy for those who fall within the latency period. The main consideration for accepting children for group therapy is their capacity for social hunger and whether they have a potential need to gain acceptance by peers. A combined activity program and verbal therapy is commonly used for preadolescents and adolescents. Very few therapists have attempted to treat adolescent boys and girls together[14], undoubtedly because of possible sexual acting out. An important trend in children's treatment has been the concurrent treatment of mothers individually or in groups or, if possible, both parents. The scheduling of treatment hours for children's and parents' groups at precisely the same time has proved effective.

Selecting Patients for Group Treatment in a Social Agency Setting

Special circumstances and problems enter into the selection of patients for group treatment within a social agency setting. Most persons who go to a social agency have what they consider urgent problems in their current reality situation. They may regard the suggestion that they undergo group therapy with irritation, dismay, indignation, or some other response that is not ideal for starting a good therapeutic relationship. These clients may have had a brief or long-term relationship with a social worker or some other functionary before being referred for group therapy. The group therapist connected with the social agency is therefore likely to inherit the favorable or unfavorable feelings developed by the client during his contact with agency workers. In many instances group therapy is undertaken while another staff member continues to deal with the aforementioned current problems.

The social agency's involvement with several members of the family on a number of different levels tends to create special areas of concern for the group therapist who is also working with the family.

An extremely important consideration in social work contacts is the agency's underlying philosophy of treatment. For example, it is the policy of some social agencies to set a date for terminating contact between the client family and the agency. Such considerations seldom enter into a group therapist's ordinary practice but may loom large if he is working in this kind of agency. An increasing number of social agencies are psychoanalytically oriented, in which case more intensive relationships with the group therapist may be expected.

Democratic principles in regard to priority on waiting lists in most clinics and agencies, while commendable, may create specific problems for the group therapist. Some patients assigned to his group may bear animus toward him because of personal prejudice or for other reasons. The agency's referral system does not give the client an opportunity to choose his own therapist, which may be a sensitive point to both.

Some agencies have wisely attacked such problems by placing patients in preliminary groups for five or six weeks. This interval gives the intake staff an opportunity to learn more about the patient's behavior, problems, and needs. This observation period aids them in assigning him to a group where he will function adequately.

The Therapist in the Group

The therapist is, of course, also a member of any group he leads. He must therefore realistically consider his own value system, fears, and counter-transference reactions in assessing his suitability for leading each group. If his impressions or feelings lead to misgivings about how he may react to a certain patient or kind of patient, it is best to clarify his reactions by discussions with his supervisor before working with this patient. Otherwise his attitude and concern may be implicit to both the patient and the group.

Exigencies such as lack of funds for treatment, unavailability of other therapy groups, or a psychiatric emergency may justify placement of a patient in a group—usually in an institutional setting—even though there is reason to believe he and the therapist may not function effectively together. But in general it must be again stressed that group therapists should try to work out their problems in relation to such patients. Progress toward the best possible placement in any kind of setting depends to a great extent on how frankly each therapist faces up to his problem and feels free to discuss the case at hand with his supervisor or in a clinical conference.

References

1. DE SCHILL, S., *Introduction to Psychoanalytic Group Therapy*, 4th ed., rev. New York, American Mental Health Foundation, 1961.
2. STONE, A. R., PARLOFF, M. B., and FRANK, J. D., The use of diagnostic groups in a group therapy program. *Internat. J. Group Psychotherapy* 3:274, 1954.
3. MALAMUD, D., Educating adults in self-understanding. *Ment. Hyg.* 44:115–24, 1960.
4. SLAVSON, S. R., Criteria for selection and rejection of patients for various types of group psychotherapy. *Internat. J. Group Psychotherapy* 1:1, 1955.
5. FREEDMAN, M. B., and SWEET, B. S., Some specific features of group psychotherapy and their implications for selection of patients. *Internat. J. Group Psychotherapy* 4:355, 1954.
6. LEOPOLD, H. S., Selection of patients for group psychotherapy. *Am. J. Psychotherapy* 11:634, 1957.
7. ANTHONY, E. J., Age and syndrome in group psychotherapy. *J. Long Island Consultation Center*, 1:3, 1960.
8. FURST, W., Homogeneous versus heterogeneous groups. *Internat. J. Group Psychotherapy* 2:120, 1951.
9. GLATZER, H. T., The relative effectiveness of clinically homogeneous and heterogeneous psychotherapy groups. *Internat. J. Group Psychotherapy*, 3:258, 1956.
10. HULSE, W. C., Dynamics and techniques of group psychotherapy in private practice. *Internat. J. Group Psychotherapy* 4:65, 1954.
11. WOLMAN, B. B., Group psychotherapy with latent schizophrenics. *Internat. J. Group Psychotherapy* 3:301, 1960.
12. KADIS, A. L., and WINICK, C., The role of the deviant in the therapy group. *Internat. J. Soc. Psychiatry*, 6:277, 1960.
13. GINOTT, H., *Group Psychotherapy with Children*. New York, McGraw-Hill, 1961.
14. ACKERMAN, N. W., Group psychotherapy with a mixed group of adolescents. *Internat. J. Group Psychotherapy* 3:249, 1955.

the first group session: 6
preparation, procedure,
and structuring

A FIRST group therapy meeting in any kind of setting presents characteristic difficulties since the new experience of mutual exposure inevitably engenders anxiety in both patient and therapist. When a patient's anxiety exceeds his tolerance level, he may attempt to protect himself by taking flight from the group or even from treatment altogether. The form of his flight depends upon his ingenuity and personality. It is therefore essential that the therapist be aware of the range of responses and resistances commonly encountered in the initial group session so that he may be better prepared to meet and cope with them.

Thorough preparation of the patient for a first group meeting may help to contain his anxiety. Such preparation is especially important in institutional settings. The form of preparation depends on the patient's history and any previous psychotherapy experience, and on the therapist's philosophy and approach, *e.g.*, does he consider the group as a separate entity, or as an adjunct of individual therapy? In addition, it depends on whether the patient will be in group therapy only or will have both group and individual sessions: (*1*) with the same therapist (combined treatment); or (2) with different therapists (conjoint treatment).

Initial Resistance as Manifested in Patient's Questioning

The patient will have many questions before entering a group which may or may not be verbalized: "I am too shy; what will I do in a group since I can't seem to express myself?" . . . "How can I tell strangers my problems?" . . . "Will I ever be able to tell them about my extra-marital affair?" . . . "How can I tell them I'm a homosexual?" . . . "What will I do if they pressure me to talk?" . . . "What will I do if they attack me?" . . . "How can I trust people I don't even know?"

The patient's anxiety may also manifest itself in questions about the mechanics of group procedure: "Where are we going to meet?" . . . "Shall I go early or give the others a chance to get there first?" . . . "Will you (the therapist) be there early?" . . . "What do I do when I get there?" . . . "Where will I put my coat?" . . .

A young woman said: "Do we have to keep on coming once the group is started? I may not feel like it or maybe I'll be sick. I wouldn't mind joining the group but hate to think I'd have to stick it out whether I wanted to or not." Her statement was a clue to her feeling of being trapped by her own family, which came out in later sessions. The group was a symbol of the family from which she had vainly tried to escape.

The form of each patient's defense mechanism is expressed in the role he wishes to assume in the group. One patient said during the first interview: "I'm not naïve about psychotherapy. Naïve people bore me. Is this group on my level? What I need is challenge; I can't stand parlor chat. You probably think I'm contemptuous of others." This man's desire to be superior to the other patients presaged his later domineering attitude in the group.

The way in which the therapist senses and responds to the patient's primary reactions, doubts and curiosity about the first session and his placement in a particular group will have a considerable effect on the extent of his anxiety.

Introduction of the Mechanics and Procedures for Group Meetings

The intake interview at which the patient is told that he will enter a group may be very important in forming his attitudes toward the group. It is advisable for the therapist to go into some detail on the mechanics and "housekeeping" procedures. The hour, length of time, frequency, and day of the week should be made specific and clear, as well as the meeting place, how early the patient may arrive, mode of address of the members, and whether the therapist will be present when the members arrive. Equally or even more important are the feeling and tone communicated by the therapist and the rapport he establishes with the patient. They have a great effect on how the patient approaches the first session.

The briefing of potential group members will, of course, take into account the therapeutic setting. In institutions, various ancillary personnel such as receptionists and attendants may be responsible for getting the patient to his therapy sessions, so they must be informed of the arrangements that are made. At Veterans' Administration or other quasi-military institutions, it is customary to tell the patient in an authoritative way: "Beginning next week, I will see you every Monday from 1:30 to 3:30 in a group with six others."

In state hospitals, the psychotherapist also usually gives explicit directions to the patient as well as to the attendants concerned: "Next Monday, I will see you from 1:30 to 3:30 P.M. with some other patients, in Room 10. Your attendant, Jimmy, will remind you and take you to the room."

In an outpatient clinic, the usual method is to tell the patient that group therapy is likely to help him. If the patient will enter one of the therapist's groups, he may explain its advantages: "In a group, you'll be able to ventilate and share your conflicts and problems with others. Since we know each other pretty well, and I know this group, I believe it will work out advantageously for you." In case of referral to another therapist's group, he will usually comment that the therapist is well qualified and the patient is likely to gain much from working with him.

The therapist must realize that the more anxiety a patient exhibits at the prospect of entering a group, the more he will need preparation and working through of resistance[1]. One way of reducing anxiety is to say something like this: "I'm sure that you're anxious and you may be even more uneasy before next Wednesday. But, in spite of your apprehension, you'll find that being in this group will help you. There will be other people who have problems like yours." Another way of minimizing anxiety about the first sessions is to explain beforehand that every person who joins a therapy group has reservations of one kind or another. A usual reaction is the wish to leave the group between the first and tenth session, stating that: "This is not the group for me," or "I am not for this group," or "Group therapy is not for me." The therapist may say: "Such a reaction often means that something very important is going on within a patient and his feelings should be ventilated in the group. If you find you can't verbalize you feelings to the members, please speak with me individually." This suggestion prevents many patients from dropping out of the group. They frequently say to the therapist: "If you hadn't warned me about this reaction, I would have simply stayed away, perhaps not even getting in touch with you or the group to give my reasons."

Group therapists often prefer to limit discussion in the initial interview to time and place of meetings and fees, adding a few words about group therapy as an aid toward solution of the patient's problems. They believe this method lets them find out how the patient responds to a new prototypal situation. His anxieties and transference reactions or parataxic distortions can then manifest themselves during therapy. These group therapists try to avoid answering objections and direct questions charged with meaning and instead deal with the threatening anticipations expressed. They assure each patient that all prospective group members have similar feelings, that each person in a group says only what he is ready to say at any particular time, and that the group therapy process fosters a feeling of mutual trust which includes respect for the confidences of all concerned.

Setting of Limits

The initial structuring of a group also may include the setting of limits, with the degree of restriction varying widely according to the setting, the type of group and its goal, the training and orientation of the therapist. Although some hospitals and clinics permit a therapist wide latitude, they are more likely to have administrative policies which set bounds on his freedom. In some agencies, a rather rigid policy requires that each patient receive the following instructions for group therapy.

You have to be here each Friday from 1:30 to 3:30. You are to make no other arrangements for this time. If you miss more than four meetings without acceptable cause, you will be dropped from treatment. Upon arriving, you will sit in the waiting room until called into the treatment room at 1:30. You are not to put your feet on the furniture. Smoking is permitted, but ashes and cigarettes must be confined to ashtrays. All litter is to be deposited in proper receptacles. This is a publicly-endowed clinic and these rules must be followed.

In private practice the appropriate limits usually are those which create the most comfortable atmosphere for the therapist to conduct sessions. There are group therapists who prefer to place few limitations on group members. They believe that all behavior, including attendance and any form of acting out, is material for analysis and should not be restricted beforehand, either directly or indirectly. When a patient starts to light a cigarette, the therapist can say: "What makes you want to smoke right now? Instead of smoking, I wish you'd tell us." Other group therapists, however, place rigid limits on group members, feeling that any overt acting out manifestation is destructive and interferes with psychotherapeutic progress.

"Breaking the rules" may result in denial on the part of the patient or, in some cases, his expulsion from the group. One therapist may prohibit smoking during the group session because he feels this hampers therapy by dissipating anxiety and interfering with its verbal expression. Another may prohibit any personal extragroup contact of members even to the point of requiring them to leave one at a time, since he believes such relationships interfere with the "purity" of the therapeutic process.

Each rationale for such limitations may have an opposing counterpart. Thus, everything is material for analysis, *but* limitations are necessary if only to protect the patient from destructive behavior (by himself or others) and to protect the therapist from legal hazards. Smoking dissipates anxiety, *but* the patient must have some means of keeping his anxiety at a tolerable level. Outside contacts spoil the purity of the therapeutic relationships, *but* they may aid the patient in both accepting help from and offering help to other patients, thus diminishing his close dependency upon the therapist. The therapist must evaluate the wisdom of each limitation. If there are to be regulations and/or restrictions regarding the group, the results of violating them must be made clear prior to and again at the first meeting.

Groups that have relatively limited goals, like guidance and counseling groups, are likely to receive fairly structured preparation. Groups that have relatively extensive goals, like psychoanalytic groups, are likely to receive less or no structured preparation, so that all material brought up will be available for analysis. The therapist's instructions to the patient should be based on his rationale of group treatment and the needs of the particular group and its members.

The First Group Meeting

The opening session will set the stage for the total therapeutic process and movement for the group, just as the first act of a play sets its tone. The therapist's perception of himself as a group therapist as well as his goals and ambitions will determine the pace, content, and direction of this session and his treatment orientation and philosophy. He may ask the patients to meet and introduce themselves before he arrives or he may be present and introduce them to each other or ask each member to introduce himself to the others. Some therapists elect to remain completely passive, permitting the patients to handle their introductions as they wish.

Many therapists find it useful to introduce themselves and then ask the patients to follow suit. First names are often used to preserve anonymity. The therapists may introduce patients by name or ask them to make their own introductions and permit them to say what they wish about themselves. The sequence of introductions may depend on whether the therapist is in the room when the patients enter individually or whether he enters after all have assembled. Some therapists prefer to be called by their first names, believing that this tends to make the sessions more informal and diminishes their role as an authority image, thus encouraging freer communication. Many therapists think it wise to speak explicitly about the confidentiality of the content of group sessions.

Some therapists begin the opening session by simply stating that the group offers members an opportunity to talk about their feelings and eventually to understand their own patterns of behavior. It is not necessary for any person to feel compelled to reveal something he wants to keep to himself, but communicating freely is likely to help him gain understanding of his problems. Thus, the therapist can indicate his desire for the patients to bring up and discuss dreams, day dreams, fantasies, body sensations, and other unconscious material by merely asking, if no one brings any up spontaneously, "Any dreams?"; or "You sit so tight," or "You clasped your hands so the knuckles are white." Thus, the group members can be helped to become aware of their body tensions and nonverbal expressions and the meaning of them.

The first group session almost invariably brings forth familial and familiar *déjà vu* reactions of considerable intensity[2]. In any new or threatening group situation, patients are likely to look for something in their earlier experiential world and identify with it. They also look for similarities in each other and this unverbalized search is usually behind their questions during the opening session. "Is there another teacher in the group?" . . . "Has anybody a migraine headache like mine?" . . . "Is anybody else here not married?" . . . "Is anybody as sick as I am?" These are typical surface questions by which the patient is communicating something like, "Let's get acquainted, so we'll know who's who and what's what. Will you be able to understand me, I wonder." The patient has a profound need to identify with someone and the therapist can be continually alert to how this need is expressed or concealed by the patient.

In noninstitutional settings, the therapist's first group often consists of patients from his individual practice. These patients have known the therapist for varying periods of time, but not each other. In all probability, the patient has previously been told that a group might help him to make better progress in resolving his specific problem. Resistances, separation fears, somatic manifestations, and fear of abandonment are likely to be provoked by the prospect of the group. The therapist should take as many hours as the patient needs in order to work through his defenses, initial resistance, and new transference reactions, before the group begins. The longer a patient has been with a therapist, the stronger are his dependency ties and his fear of "losing" the therapist in the new group situation.

The group therapist, whether in a hospital, agency, or in private practice, is usually regarded by the patient with a combination of awe and dependency. Once in the group, familial and familiar reactions have an opportunity to come to the fore. A passive-dependent patient who has been cooperative and worked on a positive level in individual therapy may suddenly launch an attack on another member or on the therapist in the opening group session. This change in the nature of his transference may arouse counter-transference reactions in the therapist. The patient's group behavior often differs from what might have been expected on the basis of his behavior in individual treatment. The threat of the familial situation posed by the group may create a need in the patient to regain his previous one-to-one relationship with the therapist.

In the opening group therapy session or sessions, a patient may exaggerate his actual pain and distress in order to "force" the therapist to focus on him. Silence offers another means of gaining attention. Patients use these and many other mechanisms to get the therapist to heed their individual or collective dependency needs. Failure to satisfy these transference needs frequently results in various forms of individual and group resistance.

Among the themes that usually emerge in initial meetings are those of dependency, independence, trust, questioning of peers, need for "safety," and a quest for the ideal parent. They occur whether the therapist is active or inactive, or plays a permissive or restrictive role.

There are patients who may begin to participate in a group by gingerly presenting surface problems. They look to the therapist for guidance on the propriety of their communication level. They also evaluate the contributions of each group member in terms of his emotional consonance and dissonance with themselves. These evaluations will be expressed both verbally and nonverbally. Nonverbal communication may include facial expressions, movement in a chair away from or toward others, such over expressions of anxiety as restlessness and brow-mopping, and similar activities.

Group Climate

The group climate evolves from many factors, among which are the role assumed by the therapist, limitations and restrictions of behavior in and outside of the session, the therapist's handling of the group members' reactions, responses, and interrelationships. The therapist tries to foster a group climate in which both he and the patients will be most comfortable.

The therapist's aim is to start a dynamic process in which group members can help each other express feelings, elicit transferences, and analyze resistances centered around material that is emotionally significant to them. It is to be hoped that these happenings in their past life will be expressed comprehensively, although at first the therapist may find it necessary to help some patients verbalize them.

During this interchange, the therapist's attitude is most important. If he is optimistic, confident, and friendly, and appears at ease in the group, his attitude will make the patients feel more at ease with each other and give them a sense of having found a "safe harbor." Without taking over, he can elicit further reactions by saying to one patient, "I wonder if you'll be a little more explicit" or to the group, "Perhaps you can comment on Jack's problems in his job."

However, the therapist will do well to be moderately passive when it comes to the factual content of revelations made in this initial session, and to avoid sensitive areas that could release a flood of feeling which may render the group helpless since it is not yet ready to cope with intense feelings. The therapist's third ear and third eye must be alert to signs of discomfort that he may help assuage and halting phrases that he may help clarify in an unobtrusive manner.

In some new groups, the therapist continues in a directive role for some time. Such groups usually receive preparation and education in how to work together in therapy. The therapist is the focal point and the group is therapist-centered. Patients attempt to question him, but he does not always have the answer and may ask the others to answer. He may actively want to provide support and may encourage each member to relate to him or to the other members. He sometimes asks very direct questions, such as: "Is there anybody who has similar difficulties with his or her children?"

When a patient mentions a dream, the therapist may ask that he recount it. If he wishes to avoid analyzing the dream, he may ask the patient what it means to him. After the patient responds, the therapist may decide, for therapeutic reasons, to delay or avoid exploration of the dream by keeping the discussion on a manifest level or not giving an active response.

Some therapists deliberately assume a passive role as one means of eliciting anxiety, questioning, and negative reactions. In this event, the members generally become very anxious and start asking a variety of questions. Manifestations of both aggressive and passive dependency will be heightened in such a group.

Termination of First Session

The final fifteen minutes should be reserved for termination of the opening session. This period is especially important because it ushers in subsequent sessions and gives the therapist an opportunity to add a word of encouragement and accomplishment; to state the limits decided on regarding group behavior and communication on the outside; and to summarize the content of the session and outline various procedures for later use. In addition, he may ask for reactions to the first session: anxiety about what each patient said and thinks he should have said, comparisons with other patients, additional associative thoughts, feelings and fantasies about the group members, or dreams. If the therapist senses that the session has aroused intolerable anxiety, he will take time to allay or counteract it as best he can. The closing of the first session also provides a chance to remind the group members of the arrangements for subsequent meetings.

One method of terminating a group session is Alexander Wolf's technique of "going around," in which members are asked to tell their feelings and thoughts about each other[3]. This ventilation is most useful in preventing the accumulation of intense feelings. At the same time, the therapist must recognize that members' expressions of extremely strong positive or negative feelings about each other or the therapist may threaten the group's very existence.

Here are some typical remarks made by patients at the end of an opening session: "When I came I thought everyone would be crazy, and I was surprised to see people looking nice" . . . "Rose makes me think of my beautiful younger sister. They even dress alike—very sporty and simple" . . . "I really don't like John; I'm afraid I'll get into a real hassle with him. He looks so angry. Usually I'm afraid of people like John and pick a fight with them. I hope it won't happen here."

A few minutes before the meeting ends, the therapist may say something like: "I think we are a good group. As you can see, there are many common problems here which we will continue to explore. I am looking forward to seeing you Thursday at the same time."

Some Typical Problems of First Sessions

In the opening session, both the therapist and the patients are very uneasy and even fearful about anticipated protracted silence. This silence can always be dealt with. After a few moments the therapist may ask, "Why so quiet? Are you waiting for me?" At least one patient will respond, perhaps by saying, "Maybe we're scared." Others will then join in, identifying with this patient who admits his fears and a chain of interaction is started.

The therapist must be alert to the many demands for direct answers, instructions, and guidance that will be made. It is usually more rewarding for the therapist to try to understand what lies beneath the members' questions and demands for guidance than to respond directly. Once patients feel that he understands their ill-expressed or even unexpressed longings and disturbances, their needs for protection and assurance, they are more willing and able to conduct explorations on their own.

The therapist, acting as a stimulator or catalyst, will probably find that future meetings are made smoother if he observes a few cautions: (1) Let group members voice and set their own expectations, stating what they hope to gain from therapy both individually and as a group. (2) When patients press for pat answers, toss back the ball. This helps to reaffirm their faith in their own ability to cope with problems. In this regard, he may ask what role the group expects him to play and why. (3) Watch for characteristic and individual patterns evidenced by reactions of the members. It will be found that each tries to make his presence felt in some way—by humorous sallies, by deep and thoughtful silence, by ingratiating remarks or actions, by a display of knowledge, by psychologically brilliant observations, by outright domination, and similar maneuvers. These clues will be helpful to both therapist and patients during their ensuing close and concentrated work together.

In the opening session, the therapist should stimulate effective encounters but avoid interpretation of material. His ability to elicit free expression of feelings will, in great degree, encourage multiple transferences and meaningful interactions. He may wish to emphasize that the more actively and spontaneously the patients participate, the more profitable will be their therapeutic experience.

One of the therapist's principal concerns at this early stage is forging the disparate members into a cohesive group. Despite their widely varying personalities, problems, and interests, he can point out their desire and need for treatment is a strong common bond. When he picks up the prevailing mood (whether expressed explicitly or not) he may sympathetically comment on what they are experiencing, then help them to bring their attitudes, thoughts, and feelings out into the open. Another method is to encourage members to help each other, or nod in agreement when one makes a positive comment about another. These seemingly small points serve to bolster the member's recognition of and respect for each other's intuitive perceptions. The sooner they can communicate in a friendly manner, the sooner they will develop a sense of belonging to the group.

From the very moment a patient enters therapy, both conscious and unconscious resistance factors may be expected to appear on the surface. Conscious resistances may include the refusal to tell about extramarital relationships, sexual deviations, or anything that is likely to be disapproved by either the family prototype or society. These patients are preferably kept in combined treatment until they feel secure with the group members. The more intense the conscious resistance, the greater the accumulation of anxiety and group pressure. As anxiety mounts, the patient seeks to reinstate past defense mechanisms in order to protect his threatened ego. This defense may take the form of acting out in an attempt to destroy the group.

One example of the complexity of this acting out after the first group session was provided by a homosexual. He outwardly appeared to be very masculine and held an important business position. After the first week of group treatment, he was caught molesting a young boy in a public lavatory. He then went to a group member to borrow

money in order to buy his way out of this predicament. He was intoxicated when he came to the second session and said to the group:
"After I talk with you, you will all be disgusted with me and want to
get rid of me."

The members, feeling threatened, said: "You can't come in a
drunken state. We won't let you in." When the members' anxiety became virtually intolerable, the therapist said: "Alex, you succeeded in
making your 'family' afraid of you, as usual. You appear to be frightened and want them to reject you rather than to reject us."

At this point, the patient laughed and said: "You're a smart cookie."
The therapist then said: "What is so frightening to you here in this
group?"

As the group's anxiety abated, Alex was able to ventilate his fears
about revealing that he was a homosexual, and exhibited his transference resistance toward the group and the analyst as family prototypes. In the early stages of a group, there are frequent manifestations
of acting out, attempts to provoke anger in the group or the therapist,
and inability to loosen hostile dependency ties.

Anxiety tends to reach a high pitch during the first several sessions
as patients re-experience emotionally stirring or painful familiar and
familial situations from the past. The therapist frequently begins the
second session by referring to the degree of anxiety engendered by the
first meeting and persisting during the intervening week. In soliciting
reactions to the previous session, he may say: "I know it won't be easy
to share our feelings about it, but it will undoubtedly be helpful for
all of us." In this way, common anxiety experiences may be brought
up that would otherwise remain unexpressed.

In an opening session that goes well, seeds are planted for culti-
vation of a nonthreatening atmosphere. The therapist has made it
clear that he wishes to remain in the background, and members have
grasped the idea that the therapy they seek and need will include
self-examination of their attitudes, anxieties, and life pattern.

References

1. ORMONT, L. R., The preparation of patients for group psychoanalysis. *Am. J.*
   Psychotherapy 11:841, 1957.
2. KADIS, A. L., Early childhood recollections as aids in group psychotherapy.
   J. Individual Psychol. 13:182, 1957.
3. WOLF, A., The psychoanalysis of groups. *Am. J. Psychotherapy* 3:213, 1949.

some group phenomena 7

A THERAPY group is a special kind of group because it has the special communality of a therapeutic purpose and because it develops multiple transference relationships in the presence of a therapist. Any group, for therapy or other purposes, is a group because there is some kind of interactional or interpersonal or affective relationship which exists among its members. A number of people sitting in a train who have never before seen each other and are not talking to each other do not constitute a group because they have neither an interactional nor interpersonal nor affective relationship to each other. If there were an emergency, like the train being stalled in a tunnel, the people in the car would probably begin to communicate and develop relationships with each other and thus become a group. If the car were stalled long enough for its passengers to project predisposing emotional responses onto others, the people in the train would begin to demonstrate some characteristics of a therapy group. The therapy group is a situation that forces its members to transpose feelings from earlier situations onto group members.

There are a number of different points of view on the ways by which a therapy group develops relationships among its members and moves along its therapeutic course. Differences in patients, therapist, and circumstances under which the group meets all will contribute to its therapeutic course. Whatever his school of therapeutic orientation, and whatever kind of group he has, the therapist's role is always to focus on the exploration, and whatever prevents the exploration, of

79

each patient's problems and to help the patients to explore why they are not working through their problems. Different kinds of problems are of interest to different kinds of therapy groups. Depending on what school of therapy he adheres to, a therapist will perceive different kinds of relationships developing among the members of the group.

The group's life cycle has been variously described. Bach has suggested that the group process unfolds itself in a relatively linear way, which is relatively predictable and which has some schematic landmarks[1]. He sees seven phases in the group's "theragnostic" work: sensing a behavior problem, acknowledging it, reactive avoidance or suppression of the problem, pinning down the instigation for the behavior problem, recognizing unconscious needs, demonstrating the reality of defensive needs, and discovering ways of utilizing the environment. Stoute sees three phases in a group's development: resistance, developing discussion of deep problems, and freedom and friendliness[2].

Three phases of a group's development are identified by Cholden: searching in order to understand limits, noting provocative events in the group, and discussing the genesis of emotions and conflicts[3]. Another trichotomy of phases was identified by Taylor as self-revelation, transforming personal into group problems, and group interpretation[4].

Four phases in a group's development have been reported by other students. Wender sees the phases as intellectualization, transference among patients, catharsis, and group interest[5]. Dreikurs identifies the establishment of relationships, interpretation by the therapist, the beginning of self-understanding, and reorientation[6]. Abrahams sees relationships related to the past, interaction, lessening of resistance, and therapeutic mutuality[7].

Perhaps one eclectic way of defining the group process is that it is the way in which the group expresses itself in its therapeutic course within the parameters which its emotional climate and members make possible. The therapeutic course of one group is likely to vary from that of another group because the combination of a particular therapist with specific group members creates specific climates.

The group process includes the focus of group communication by the therapist. The group communicates on a variety of different levels at the same time. One level is the literal one, concerned with the obvious manifest content of what is said. The second is the inter-personal level, concerned with elements such as status and role, along with the more formal content of a communication and its direction. The third level is concerned with the unconscious significance of what is said and thus with the symbolic implications of the other group members; *i.e.*, does a patient experience and react to another patient as a symbolic sister prototype? A psychoanalytic group therapist will focus mainly on communication on the third level, whereas the therapist of a guidance group, for example, would emphasize communication on the first and second levels.

Let us take Tim, a patient in a group, who comes in, sits down, and says to the patient on his right, Joe: "How are you today?" On the literal level he is merely asking a friendly and uncomplicated question about how his fellow patient is. On the interpersonal level, Tim may have sat next to Joe and greeted him respectfully because Joe is a high status person outside the group as well as in it, and Tim may be observing the pecking order of the group. On the level of the unconscious, Tim may have addressed the question to Joe because he identified strongly with a dream which Joe reported at the last group session, or because he sees Joe as a symbolic father prototype and is being friendly in order to avoid hostility which he anticipates from Joe. Tim may be communicating on one or two or all three of these levels in the single communication. It is this complexity of therapeutic group processes which makes it so difficult to describe group phenomena. One way of describing these phenomena is through what can be called *G-responses*.

G-Responses

Thousands of groups have met for therapeutic purposes in the decades since group therapy began to emerge as a separate procedure. As a result of so many groups having met and having been through certain nodal experiences, various central response situations have occurred often enough to be identifiable as unique and indigenous to the therapy group. These responses can be called *G-responses* for Group responses, to describe their recurring and ubiquitous nature. There are various nodal points in the group therapy process at which there is a special likelihood that the group climate will be modified or that a schematic response will occur. These special circumstances are unique to group therapy and do not occur in other kinds of therapy or other situations. For this reason we call them G-responses. Their repetitive nature makes it even more important and useful to examine their nature and dimensions.

These G-responses provide special opportunities to observe how a therapy group responds as a group to a wide variety of change and movement situations in what is clearly an adaptational manner. It is likely to be a kind of homeostatic response, which has as its goal the maintenance of group equilibrium and the maintenance of whatever level of anxiety the group can sustain. The therapy group can be said to function like a self-sealing tire, the internal pressure of which constantly moves toward any hole in its wall in order to seal it and prevent the air from getting out of the tire.

Knowledge of G-responses may be used differentially in different kinds of therapy groups. In guidance and counseling groups in which ego functioning is the major goal, knowledge of the G-responses represents a valuable tool which the therapist can use to direct the group interaction. In psychoanalytic groups, the therapist would keep the G-responses in mind, to be used in the ongoing group process rather than used to limit the interaction. Knowledge of these responses is almost a necessity for any consideration of the homeostasis of a group.

Homeostasis

Almost all G-responses represent attempts at some kind of homeostasis. The group constantly seeks to strike a balance among the anxieties of its different members. This balance represents a kind of homeostasis which keeps the anxiety of the members on a tolerable level, just as the body's endocrine machinery represents an attempt to keep the body's internal secretions balanced. The special qualities of a therapy group's climate help to create group reactions to possible points of disruption in the group's homeostasis. Like a person, the group seeks an equilibrium which is minimally upsetting.

The group process is a tangled fabric of pushing and pulling, hate and love, aggression and passivity, coolness and warmth. All of these different emotional directions serve the purpose of strengthening the therapeutic cohesiveness of the group. The emotional reactions of a therapy group can result in a therapeutic climate that permits working out and working through conflicts. It is a climate, however, which is likely to be constantly modified by anyone, including the therapist. A group in which there is a rigid consistency, be it conformity or antagonism, is not likely to be a group with much therapeutic movement, even though it does have consistency.

The special qualities of the emotional communication which occurs among group members tax the resources of the English language because there is no one word which is adequately descriptive. It is analogous to the process of osmosis, inasmuch as there is a kind of constant flow or interchange through barriers. It is also like osmosis in that much of the communication between members of a group takes place with people "getting things through the skin." This is one metaphoric way of expressing the nonverbal nature of much of the experience which may be obtained in a therapy group.

Just as homeostasis maintains the inner equilibrium of the body, so the group situation maintains a certain balance which at any one time is likely to be appropriate for the group. The needs of any one individual may not be met by the homeostasis of the group at any particular time. Each member constantly seeks to mold the group in a direction which will meet his own needs and might be said to be engaging in almost a process of suction. Sometimes the individual's needs involve an attempt to keep the group on a particular theme and to avoid any change in its climate. Another member of the same group may feel that his needs will be met more effectively if the group leaves this theme or attempts to change the climate. This kind of conflict must be resolved in the best interests of the group, even though at least one of the members will be relatively displeased by the manner in which it is resolved. The group climate may be modified by the therapist, who feels that he knows best what is constructive for the group and changes the topic of discussion himself. When members of the group take action themselves in order to achieve change in the group climate, the change is likely to be less effective than if the therapist had suggested it. The displeasure of the members is likely to be greater in response to a suggestion for change from a therapist than from other patients. Passive dependent patients are likely to be displeased if any one but the therapist initiates a cnange, although the degree of their displeasure will depend on the degree of their transference.

Every member of the group is seeking to create and sustain a milieu in which his needs will be met. In effect he is saying, "I want the group to give complete satisfaction to me." This is coupled with his active and expressed interest in seeking change while at the same time seeking to avoid change. It can be said that, from one point of view, the most important single force in a therapy group is the maintenance of status quo of the group members. They may say that they want change, but actually may find it very difficult to make it possible for themselves to change. The fear of change may have a paralyzing effect on a patient. Part of the climate of a therapy group consists of the tension provided by the patients' resistance to change and the powerful counterforce provided by the desire for change, which also is true of treatment in individual therapy.

Homeostasis in a therapy group is most threatened by a change agent. In a group therapeutic situation the therapist is primarily the person who has the leading role of change agent. The change agent in the group is the person who makes it possible for others to change. He or she largely does so on the basis of the transference relationship which develops within the group. In the therapy group the change agent may be different people at different times. In addition to the therapist it may be another patient with whom there is a particularly strong transference relationship which is especially meaningful. A therapy group which has achieved a satisfactory homeostasis is likely to have achieved a strong feeling of cohesion. The dimension of cohesion by itself is not necessarily desirable or undesirable, from the point of view of the effects of the change agent in the group. In terms of the nature and progress of the group, it may or may not be a therapeutic adjuvant. Cohesion may be used by the members to resist change. Or, like T. S. Eliot's little men huddling together nervously, the group members may exhibit cohesion because of the need to obtain strength by group reinforcement.

Some kinds of cohesion in a group may be based on the hostility which exists among individuals. The hostility among the members of a therapy group may serve to bind them together emotionally, just as the liking of some members may bind another group at varying times of the therapeutic movement. Any given group may oscillate between different kinds of climate within a relatively short period. Its climate may be disassociated and withdrawn one week and relatively enthusiastic and warm a few sessions later. The therapist can use his observation of the climate of the group as an element in his interpretation to the members. A special occasion for this kind of interpretation is when there are one or two group members who do not share the prevailing emotional climate, so that the contrast between the rest of the group and the one or two members is relatively visible. One dimension, and perhaps the most important one, in any consideration of group cohesion and climate, is that of transference.

Multiple Transference

Perhaps the most widespread of G-responses is that of multiple transference. A central concept in most modern schools of psychotherapy is transference, or the transfer onto the therapist of emotions from earlier situations. Freud regarded his description of the patient's transference as a projection onto the analyst of emotions toward members of the patient's former or current family as perhaps the subtlest concept he had developed. S. R. Slavson adapted and modified some of Freud's concepts for the group situation and made what Wilfred Hulse has called a great and permanent contribution to the subject[8]. While Slavson contends that the group setting dilutes the transference, Hulse has observed that there is no reason to assume that the transference reaction which group members have is necessarily more diluted than that which they have toward the therapist in individual treatment[9]. He believes, however, that the primary transference is to the therapist and all others are derivative.

Inasmuch as all psychotherapy is predicated on the relationship between therapist and patient, it is only natural that the transference relationship should be seen to be assuming a variety of forms which lend themselves to a variety of different kinds of explanation. The central role of transference in group psychotherapy has been noted, among others, by Altshuler[10], Bion[11], Ezriel[12], Foulkes[13, 14], Hadden[15], Klapman[16], Pederson-Krag[17], Powdermaker and Frank[18], Marsh[19], Sternbach[20], Sutherland [21], and Wolf[22]. The uniqueness of the special emotional tension system created by multiple transference has been noted.

Group therapy conducted by therapists of various schools will reveal different kinds of transference phenomena. Horney-oriented therapists will tend to see their patients as moving toward, against, or away from people, in the group situation[23]. Their major concern is not so much the genesis of a particular transference relationship as on the manner in which the interaction is occurring at a given time. Therefore, perception of group transference activities will center around the vector of movement.

Sullivanian therapists will see their patients engaging in parataxic distortions and perceiving each other in a distorted way based on their functional need to distort (parataxic) the people they see[24]. Parataxic distortion is used to explain why patients in a group sometimes see qualities in a group member which other patients do not see. Sullivanians would say that specific kinds of childhood experience probably lead to parataxic distortions and thus to group transference.

In the psychoanalytic group which seeks to effect basic character change the transference relationship among group members and therapists is likely to include dreams, daydreams, fantasies, and body sensations, as well as the other verbal interaction which characterizes all therapy groups. In the guidance group, with its relatively limited goals, the transference relationship will be contained within and be mediated by the relatively structured comments of the group members, with a relative minimum of emotional reactions. Groups with other goals may develop transference relationships within the framework of their level of communication, and as a reflection of their frequency of meetings, the length of life of the group, the members of the group, and the therapist. Any one patient in a therapy group is likely to develop multiple transferences to a variety of different persons in the group, each of whom may have a different symbolic meaning to him. Multiple transference is the process by which each patient responds transferentially to what Alexander Wolf has called "the variously provocative characteristics of the multiple personalities in the group." The different people in the group permit each patient to respond to a wide variety of transference stimuli.

The nature of the group transference may readily be seen in a situation where a number of group members frown on and call attention to the different elements of a single repetitive behavior pattern in which a patient engages. By contrast, in individual treatment the therapist is the only person available to detect and point out reaction patterns to the patient. Different group members are likely to select particular elements of the behavior which they will react to in the patient. These elements are likely to be reflections of their unique transference relations to the patient. When a given pattern of behavior is repetitively engaged in with a group of patients, it is being simultaneously presented to a number of different persons, each of whom is in a different transference relationship to the patient who provides the repetitive stimulus. Each one is thus likely to comment on a different aspect of the patient's behavior.

Multiple transference may lead to the recognition of a familiar family relationship or situation which is sparked by one or more patients. It may, however, generate such great anxiety in a patient that his response will involve the expression of a characteristic defense mechanism because of the vigor of his transference reaction.

The nature of the group therapy process insures that the transference bonds in a group will be just as intense and perhaps even more complex than they are in individual therapy.

The transference relationship to the therapist in the group may differ from that in the individual treatment situation because the former is in a much more exposed position. The comfort of anonymity is denied him because his behavior, interpretations and appearance are all subject to detailed scrutiny by and observations from the members of the therapy group. He perforce has to be relatively active, compared to the individual therapist, who might let session after session go by without even one comment. His silence, of course, is not necessarily a barrier to transference relations with him.

It is obvious that the counter-transference or the emotional reaction induced in the therapist by and toward the members of his group are likely to be more complex and also more visible in the group situation than in the individual situation. Interacting with so many different kinds of people at the same time, it is logical to expect that the group therapist's reaction to the group members will be different in a number of ways from his reaction to a patient in individual treatment. Even therapists who have spent years treating someone in individual therapy may be surprised at some aspects of the patient which emerge when he goes into a group.

How does transference come about? The patient's predisposition to transference is developed by his history. The familiar-familial atmosphere and climate provided by the therapy group facilitate the experiencing and expression of transference feelings. The therapist does not have to do anything to help generate transference relationships in a therapy group any more than he does in individual treatment; it would be like taking action to see that July is a warm month in the Northern Hemisphere. When a group of people assemble for therapeutic purposes and meet regularly to discuss their problems in an atmosphere of intimacy, multiple transference just happens, without any special attempt on anyone's part to achieve it.

The relationship of the therapy group members to each other is like that of a group of brothers and sisters who have almost voluntarily found each other, rather than having been placed into the same family by biological chance. The analogy to the family is appropriate because the central basis of the transference is likely to be the patient's larger family interrelationships. The gradual unfolding of the extent to which his emotional reactions to others in the group are reflections of his relationship to "significant others" in his life is likely to be one of the most profound therapeutic experiences of the group member. The more clearly the patient's transference relationships emerge and the more clearly he appears to be transferring earlier emotional perceptions and relationships to the members of the group, the more of a stake he has in mobilizing his resources in order to protect the defenses which have in the past shored up his relationship to others.

The patients tend to respond as if they were in a familiar situation because the therapy group is, par excellence, where communication takes place in terms of the phenomena of *déjà vu*, or "I have been here before." Patients are likely to adopt toward other group members the behavior and responses which have been most acceptable in childhood. This behavior was usually "learned" in the patient's original family, and as a result it is this kind of behavior with which they are most familiar and with the manifestation of which they feel less threatened. This manifest behavior is repetitive, compulsive, and over-reactive.

As the therapy process unfolds, the patient is likely to become less comfortable with the familiar *déjà vu* role into which he originally fell, because he will be becoming aware of the transference qualities in his relationship with the other members of the group. It is the therapist's responsibility to insure that the patient's awareness of his transference relationship is relatively gradual, lest there be an unexpected flare-up of the patient's defense mechanisms of such proportions that his therapeutic progress is set back. An overly rapid confrontation of a patient with his transference behavior may lead to the patient removing himself from the ongoing group transference situation by behaving in a withdrawn manner. Such confrontations are relatively unlikely in individual treatment, but other group members may point out transference reactions to a patient and their timing may not be opportune. It is of course unfortunate if the therapist makes a transference interpretation before the patient is ready for it.

It has been pointed out how the behavior of the group therapist in the transferential situation can contribute to shifting of the transference relationship away from the therapist to various group members. He can point up transference relationships which obtain between group members and thus inferentially call attention away from himself.

It is the therapist's task to keep alert to the development of transferences and to interpret their significance. The therapist can do this without even once using the word "transference." He can communicate effectively enough without using jargon. By a focusing statement like "Grace, your reaction to Ruth's questioning—does it seem to have any relationship to anything in your life?" the therapist may effectively communicate an insight into transference. If Grace says, "Yes, that's how I always reacted to my mother," she has understood something of how transference works.

The ways in which transference manifests itself may vary during the life cycle of a group. Its manifestations change as individuals change in the group situation. Different patients may even assume different transferential roles in the group. Thus, a patient may be initially perceived as a kind of rejecting father by another patient and as a protecting father by yet another patient. He may no longer be perceived in these roles as time goes on and he and the other patients change.

Prototypical transference mechanisms are especially visible during the first five or so group sessions because of the considerable testing of the therapist and the other patients which occurs during these sessions. Each patient will be appraising and evaluating the therapist in terms of the extent to which the therapist will provide him with protection and preferential treatment. Each patient will be thinking about how the group will help him in a situation in which he is vying with others for the therapist's attention. There may be considerable initial caution about self-expression in the group because of the fear of exposure. ("What will they think of me if they know that I steal from the petty cash?") No matter how cautious the patients are, they are still likely to be engaging in the emotional reaching which constitutes transference.

The initial meetings are likely to see patients making transference identifications which are relatively familial—familiar in nature because it is this kind of response with which a patient is likely to feel most at ease. The reason for the relative ease with which transference may be visible at the commencement of a group is that in such situations any given patient may perceive and react unconsciously to some familiar characteristics in another group member, like Konrad Lorenz's bird which attacked all the birds it saw which had a little red spot. In a group situation, he almost inevitably reacts with multiple transference.

Reactive Associations

Another G-response is the reactive association. This type of association is relatively common, but unique to the group psychotherapeutic process. The reactive association may be provoked by a mood, physical action, or verbalizations of another member, members, or the total group. A case in point is a sixty-second silence within one group which followed a heated discussion among the group members. Suddenly, Jack exploded, "Goddamn it, this is just like my family when I was a kid. I don't remember how old I was or how long it lasted, but it had to take place before my mother died, when I was five. I can picture it now. My mother and father and my older brother and sister arguing and fighting with one another and then suddenly they stopped. After that, nobody spoke to anybody else for a long time. I remember wondering what had happened and how come nobody talked to me. I didn't do anything, and yet I seemed to be blamed for what had happened."

Although reactions and associations may be induced in individual sessions by visual or verbal stimuli, it is not possible to react to social climate created by other people. In individual sessions, there are no people present other than the therapist and the patient.

Defense Mechanisms

As in individual treatment, patients in a group are continually resisting treatment by defense mechanisms which can logically be regarded as G-responses. Patients in a group are likely to resist any change which involves a modification of their customary way of doing things and defense mechanisms represent the security procedures which they employ in order to fend off awareness of the need for a change, or to fend off anxiety. The defense mechanism functions like the antennae of an insect, which examine the environment for signs of danger. When the individual senses that the group situation is threatening one of his established patterns of response, his defense postures are likely to become paramount.

The more intense the threat posed to the individual by the very existence of a given person, or by what a patient says, or by an interpretation from the therapist, the more intense is his defense mechanism likely to be. The selection of the defense mechanism will almost always not be a conscious choice by the patient. It will be a reflection not only of the individual's personality, but also of the group situation at the particular time. Psychotherapy in a group can only occur to the extent that patients employ and gradually become aware of their defense mechanisms. They can hardly become aware of a defense mechanism the first time that it is employed in a therapy group after having unwittingly used it for years. But one of the features of the group communication process is the enormous impact of five or six or eight group members who continue to call a patient's attention to something he is doing. The cumulative impact of several people repeatedly observing that a patient handles certain situations by the repetitive use of a particular response pattern ultimately is likely to have a profound effect on the group member. This effect is a major component of the psychotherapeutic process.

If there is a strong enough feeling of nonacceptance from other members in a group, a patient who is met by continued resistance from other group members may modify his behavior without achieving insight into the cause and effect of the reaction pattern. The change is then likely to occur just out of the sheer cumulative effect of having a number of other people with whom he has an emotional relationship disagree with his behavior. Of course, ideally the patient should understand the meaning of his behavior and therefore change it. But for a patient to experience, even intellectually, that a behavior pattern of his is a compulsive repetition, can itself be constructive. As in many other life situations, a change in behavior may precede a change in attitudes, even though a more logical sequence would be a change in attitudes preceding a change in behavior.

Transference itself may be used as a resistance and as a defense mechanism. If a patient had a stern and overbearing father, he may transfer the complex feelings which he has toward his father to the therapist or toward another group member. The very ease with which the patient responds to cues and slips into the relationship and the assurance which he may feel because of the familiarity of the person who is reminiscent of the father, may make for a strong transference relationship. It may also make for serious difficulties when there is occasion to make the patient aware of the nature of the relationship to the therapist or group member and ultimately to the father whom he symbolically represents. That which is most familiar and acceptable is likely to be the most difficult to change, and the strength of a transference may be a powerful reason for its maintenance.

Some defenses against threat are similar to those found in individual treatment. Thus, silence is one such procedure. Group members may feel they "have nothing to say." Or they may engage in almost compulsive talking about relatively innocuous material, as one method of avoiding talking about more central and difficult material. One popular form of defense in group treatment which is unique to groups is the enthusiastic way in which some patients will comment on and analyze another patient, primarily in order to avoid any concentration on their own activities. They may use hostile questioning as defense. Aggressive outbursts may also serve to fend off difficulties.

Acting Out

There are many forms of acting out, or compulsive, repetitive behavior based on transference and impulses stirred up in treatment[25]. It is a very common G-response as well as a defense. This may range from the patient in a group who engages in acting-out behavior which is directed toward other group members, like attempting to seduce them, to behavior in nongroup situations in the patient's extragroup life situation, like trying to get arrested. A patient may do something which will lead to his getting arrested in order to threaten the group with dissolution; and the group will respond because the arrested patient is upsetting its homeostasis. Perhaps the most common form of acting out is a romantic attachment between two patients. Such romances are likely to be based on the mutual projection of fantasies rather than on more valid considerations.

Acting out is relevant as a G-response because it is so often directed at the group, either to maintain or interfere with its homeostasis, even though it might appear to be unrelated to what is happening in the group. A therapist confronted by acting out must consider what function it is serving in the group at the particular time, and how best to handle it. In the case of the romantic couple, he could either encourage discussion of the liaison as soon as he notices what is happening, or could wait for it to emerge more naturally. His decision on how to handle it will be based on his perception of what would be best for the group and the two patients at the particular time.

Not only a particular patient but sometimes the entire group or a substantial proportion of the group may engage in acting out. Unless the behavior is repetitive, it may not be true acting out. In a group, acting out always involves some motor activity. The actual behavior in which the "act-outer" engages is always destructive, but it may be used for constructive purposes, like reducing anticipated anxiety. Some patients may be able to express something by motor activity which they could not put into words.

Acting out is likely to be more common in group than in individual treatment. The presence of a number of people onto whom the patient can project transferentially, instead of one person, increases the possibility that the feelings which are unleashed may eventuate in acting out. The physical proximity of the other patients also helps to facilitate the process. In one group, two of the patients were Lew, a latent homosexual, who lived near Billie, a Lesbian. He would often drive her home in his car after the session. As a result of impulses aroused during treatment, Lew seduced Billie and provided her with a heterosexual experience that was nonthreatening to her, because she sensed

Lew's lack of true masculinity. The experience proved to be a very constructive one for both patients. The therapist perceived what was happening but did not discourage it; neither did the other group members. The therapist's own values clearly emerge in what he regards as acting out behavior.

The Carom

One G-response can be called a *carom*. In billiards there is a shot called a carom in which the cue-ball strikes successively two or more balls. This kind of multiple carom is akin to the effect on group members of the special condition of emotionally toned tension, which is occasioned by the group therapy process and which is a reflection of emotional contagion. A group member may say something which may trigger a carom. Eve, a patient who had been in a group for three months, said at the beginning of one session that "I am very disappointed that I am making so little progress. I want to live, not just talk about living in this group. It seems so unreal. I feel very depressed that so little is happening." Within minutes, every other patient in the group had voiced agreement with Eve's comment. They had all picked up her mood. Some reports have suggested that a dream may precipitate a carom[26].

Such a multiple carom may be communicated not only verbally, but also nonverbally, by posture, use of the facial expression, tone of voice, or in other ways. It may be communicated by an interchange between patient and therapist, or between two patients, which will have reverberations on a number of other patients. It may not be anything specific, but sometimes even the effect of part of a session or the atmosphere of a session on the patients in a group. The constantly changing nature of this interactive process makes it difficult to catch it in slow motion. When it is described in terms of the ongoing group process there is often difficulty in putting it into words.

We might speculate that the best way of capturing the special qualities of the process is through some analogue to time-lapse photography. In this form of photography, slight changes are detected because the individual frames are not exposed consecutively but at fixed time intervals, *e.g.*, every five seconds. One example of the carom took place in a therapy group which had been making fairly good progress but in which, at the beginning of a session, a member said that his confidence in the therapist had been severely shaken because he had attended a lecture at which the therapist had made what he considered a poor showing. Although he was relatively vague on why he thought the therapist had done badly, the other group members all began expressing their lack of confidence in the therapist.

This situation became a carom response because a group member who is expressing what he feels to be an individual response may actually be voicing the preconscious or unconscious feelings or fantasies of other patients. For the patient, fantasies are likely to be very real. Let us take the case of a patient who comments on some change in the therapist's behavior or apparent attitude. He might note, for example, that the therapist looked sleepy or not particularly interested in what was happening in the group, or apparently thinking of something else. Although other patients may have perceived the "change" in the therapist, they were unable to express it. The patient who did speak, thus voiced what a number of other patients had felt; once the idea was voiced it could not only be experienced but also discussed. The group may then follow the lead of the patient who first makes the observation.

Subgroups

One form of acting out is the formation of subgroups. This kind of G-response may occur because patients have some kind of pretherapeutic bond or association with each other like friendship or because they have a differential response to the therapist. They may form for reasons related to transference likes or dislikes, or because of a transference-based need either to support or be antagonistic to someone or something. Subgroups may form in order to facilitate action toward or against the therapist. They may represent avoidance reactions. Others may represent conformity with or acting against. Still others may involve sucking in of prototypes in order to maintain the homeostasis of the individual. Another function served by subgroups is to obtain support for acting out behavior. Subgroups may consist of as few as two people. They are subject to change with the progress of treatment.

Sometimes the members of a subgroup will sit together, while sometimes they may go out together after a session to a kaffee-klatsch. They may communicate with each other between sessions and in other ways seek to underline their separateness from the group as a whole.

Fractionation of the Group

The group experiencing itself as a series of individual members rather than as a group is a G-response. When it happens at the beginning of a group's life cycle, it is a normal response. At other times it may happen as protection against the threat of involvement with one or more members. It may mask impulsive drives which create anxiety because of conflicts over acting out. There are circumstances in which the therapist may seek to fragment the group in order to break up rigid conformity or "me-too-ism." The members experiencing themselves as a series of individuals rather than as a group may lead to a disassociation in the group climate and withdrawal and/or isolation. At such times a group member may feel that he is all alone with his problems and that the other patients and the therapist do not understand him or respond to or meet his needs. He may manifest this withdrawal behavior either by verbal or nonverbal communication. Such manifestations of withdrawal are often very significant.

Change in Status of Group Member

A major change in a member's status, like marriage, divorce, or job loss, may elicit a G-response. It may do so because such a change involves a change in the configuration of the group and thus disrupts the homeostasis which the group has established. Change is often disturbing to the other members of a group because of their identification with the member. Thus, if a patient describes losing a job, it is possible that he might make the other members anxious as they think of the possible loss of their own jobs. Any change is likely to bring the unexpected into the group in what may be regarded as disturbing by other patients.

Patients will vary in the ways in which they respond to their feeling that the group is changing. Max, a 30-year-old mechanic, reacted strongly to the news that Bob was getting married. Max had put an ashtray on a stool near his feet. He knocked the ashtray over in changing position in his chair and said suddenly, "I wish I could pick up the stool and throw it at Bob. I only put it near my feet so that I wouldn't kick him." Reactions to a change in group homeostasis may be quite violent, as was Max's.

A patient marrying may disturb the fantasies of others and occasion anxiety. Such anxiety may result from identification with the person marrying. It may stem from a feeling of loss, or it may be associated with a feeling that the marriage will bring an intruder into the group, and the group is becoming separated. In the case of unmarried patients, there may be a feeling of "Why couldn't it have been me?" All or some of these reactions may be present in addition to the joy which the group may feel at the member's marrying.

"Attacking" the Therapist

Members of a group "attacking" a leader can be understood as a G-response which is relatively common in group therapy. The exposed position of the leader makes him a very visible target. Attacking a therapist provides opportunities for examination of the reason for such attacks and their significance at any one time. Such attacks may be easier in a group than in individual treatment because a group provides mutual support for the attack. Since the nature of the group situation is especially likely to raise problems of authority and peer relationships, such problems may often be voiced in the form of an attack on the leader.

Patients may "attack" a therapist because he is spending "too much" time with the problems of a particular patient, or "not enough" time with the problems of another patient. In each such case, the symbolic function served by the attack is likely to be at least as important as its manifest content.

Attempts to Annihilate a Group Member

The attempt to annihilate a group member is a G-response to which the therapist must be alert. Such a patient may embody characteristics toward which the other patients are especially ambivalent or especially attracted. They may be attacking because of their desire to focus attention away from themselves. The attack may be a result of either a

verbal or a behavioral reaction which may be disturbing. It is a reflection of the group's need to protect its homeostasis as well as a reflection
of the individual patient's security system.

Ralph, a 37-year-old unmarried member of one group, had left his
job as an office manager in order to "take it easy." He came into the
group to announce his having quit, saying that one of the reasons he
had done so was because the group had helped him to realize that he
was being exploited by his employer. He obviously expected that the
group would praise him. Instead, they attacked him mercilessly for
quitting before he got another job, for not having married, for exploit-
ing his long-suffering girl friend, and for taking up the group's time to
discuss his job shift at the expense of the time of others who have
serious emotional problems. The therapist was able to help the group
to see why it had attacked Ralph so fiercely, in what was clearly an
overreaction.

Reaction to the Appearance of a New Member

Another G-response is the group's reaction to the appearance of a
new member. It is likely to be differential with different members
responding in individualized ways. Their responses will depend on
their own internal emotional equation at the time that the new member appears. It may vary from enthusiasm to disillusion to caution to
"You poor devil, you don't know what you're getting into!" The members often project their fantasies and expectations on the new member.

They may express feelings of superiority to him, because they have
had so much more "training." In order to preserve the homeostasis of
the group, the older members may try to get rid of a new member.
They may do this by direct attacks, by expressions of exaggerated concern, and in many other ways. The introduction of a new member into
an already existing group is almost always likely to lead to a G-response involving some expression of anxiety.

When a group has been in existence for some time and a new member is introduced, there is an unique opportunity to observe how
transference develops as group members project their feeling states on
the new member. The therapist's interpretation of transference to an
ongoing group which gets a new member differs radically from the
approach which he would use in a beginning group, in which all the

members were new to each other. The newly introduced member in an ongoing group must, of course, be treated with special caution by the therapist lest the new member be overwhelmed by the transference "sophistication" of the experienced members of the group.

The Feeling of Having Reached a Plateau

The feeling of having reached a plateau is likely to occur in any therapy group often enough to be considered a G-response. It may occur because the patients are still integrating material which has been ventilated, and are not ready to move on to new material because they may be resisting new material, or a variety of other reasons. Here again, the therapist has an opportunity to employ his expectation of a G-response to integrate his awareness of it into the group's movement.

The plateau response may occur after a period of relatively rapid therapeutic movement. It may appear after a vacation, or around holidays like Christmas and Thanksgiving, when patients are likely to feel "left out" of the enjoyment which others are experiencing. It may occur after a patient has left the group, or when there has been other change in the composition of the group.

The G-responses discussed in this chapter are examples of fairly common response sets which occur often enough in psychotherapy groups to warrant discussion. Some may and others may not occur in a particular group. The existence of G-responses does not in any way suggest that the individual reactions of group members are of great importance. The intermeshing of individual responses constitutes the G-response, although it is always possible that a given group member may not participate in any one G-response. The dynamic nature of the responses of the individuals in a group represents the raw material for the process of group therapy.

References

1. BACH, G. R., *Intensive Group Psychotherapy*. New York, Ronald, 1954, pp. 197–200.
2. STOUTE, A., Implementation of group interpersonal relationships through psychotherapy. *J. Psychol. 30*:145, 1950.
3. CHOLDEN, L., Group therapy with the blind. *Group Psychotherapy 6*:21, 1953.
4. TAYLOR, F. K., The therapeutic factors of group analytic treatment. *J. Ment. Sc. 96*:976, 1950.

5. WENDER, L., The dynamics of group psychotherapy and its application. *J. Nerv. & Ment. Dis. 84:54,* 1936.
6. DREIKURS, R., Family group therapy in the Chicago community child guidance centers. *Ment. Hyg. 35:291,* 1951.
7. ABRAHAMS, J., "Group Psychotherapy: Implications for Direction and Supervision of Mentally Ill Patients," in Theresa Muller, *Mental Health in Nursing.* Washington, Catholic Univ. Press, 1950, pp. 77–83.
8. HULSE, W. C., Multiple transferences or group neuroses, paper read to the London Group Analytic Society, July, 1960.
9. HULSE, W. C., The application of group psychotherapy in the treatment of the characterological syndrome, paper read to the Fifth Annual Institute of American Group Psychotherapy Association, New York, Jan. 25, 1961.
10. ALTSHULER, I. M., One year's experience with group psychotherapy. *Ment. Hyg. 24:190,* 1940.
11. BION, W., Experiences in groups. *Human Relations 1:314,* 1948.
12. EZRIEL, H., Notes on psychoanalytic group therapy: II. Interpretation and research. *Psychiatry 15:119,* 1952.
13. FOULKES, S. H., *Introduction to Group-Analytic Psychotherapy.* New York, Grune & Stratton, 1948.
14. FOULKES, S. H., Concerning leadership in group analytic psychotherapy. *Internat. J. Group Psychotherapy 1:319,* 1951.
15. HADDEN, S. B., Dynamics of group psychotherapy. *Arch. Neurol. Psychiat. 65:125,* 1951.
16. KLAPMAN, J. W., *Group Psychotherapy: Theory and Practice.* New York, Grune & Stratton, 1946.
17. PEDERSON-KRAG, G., Unconscious factors in group therapy. *Psychiatric Quart. 15:180,* 1946.
18. POWDERMAKER, F. and FRANK, J. D., *Group Psychotherapy.* Cambridge, Harvard Univ. Press, 1953.
19. MARSH, L. C., Group therapy and the psychiatric clinic. *J. Nerv. & Ment. Dis. 81:381,* 1935.
20. STERNBACH, O., The dynamics of psychotherapy in the group. *J. Child Psychiat. 107:195,* 1950.
21. SUTHERLAND, J. D., Notes on psychoanalytic group therapy. *Psychiatry 15:111,* 1952.
22. WOLF, A., The psychoanalysis of groups. *Am. J. Psychotherapy 3:525,* 1949; *4:16,* 1950.
23. HORNEY, K., *Our Inner Conflicts.* New York, Norton, 1945.
24. SULLIVAN, H. S., *Interpersonal Theory of Psychiatry.* New York, Norton, 1953.
25. ARONSON, M., *Acting Out in Individual and Group Psychotherapy.* New York, Postgraduate Center for Psychotherapy, 1960.
26. HOLT, H., and WINICK, C., Group psychotherapeutic experiences with clergymen, *J. Religion and Health, 1:113,* 1962.

structure and function of 8
psychotherapy groups

MANY patients with widely varying personality structure and pathology have been treated in private practice or in institutional settings by psychotherapists whose orientation and goals also vary widely.

It is only natural that different group structures have evolved as a reflection of these various approaches. A consideration of several of these structures—closed and open groups, and those used in combined and conjoint therapy—may help to clarify the group process itself.

Closed Groups

It is possible to distinguish the three main types of closed groups used for regular therapy sessions: constant membership, family prototype, and occasionally-reopened groups.

(1) *Constant membership.* Members are not permitted to leave at will, but are expected to serve the group's needs for a definite time. The time is stipulated at the outset and may range from a few months to two years.

(2) *Family prototype.* Members leave one by one when ready, detaching themselves as if from their nuclear families[1]. Since no replacements are made, the group goes out of existence when all its members have dropped out. However, in some instances the last one or two members are placed in another group or treated in other ways.

(3) *Occasionally-reopened.* Members may be added or transferred in accordance with the group's needs.

These three types of closed groups have been found particularly effective in treating homogeneous groups, which consist exclusively of one kind of patient—for example, parents, teachers[2], adolescents, or persons with the same disability, *e.g.*, heart disease or epilepsy. Their principal therapeutic goal is usually resolution of a specific common conflict or understanding of a common problem or ailment. Closed groups also lend themselves to research studies. Their relatively stable composition makes for easier follow-up and more clear-cut conclusions.

The specific qualities of closed groups almost inevitably lead to specific responses. Separation anxiety and the death theme are likely to be paramount; thus the expression of the self-preservation motif is often intensified. Some separation anxiety may be viewed as the primary neurotic problem of separation from the maternal figure. Separation from any important figure, whether it be in the nuclear family, in marriage, or in treatment, may re-elicit in the patient the same feeling of losing his original parasitic and subsequent symbiotic relationship with the mother. Carried to its extreme, separation anxiety is, of course, fear of death as the ultimate departure. A member's leaving is thus symbolically perceived by the group as a final leave-taking. Typical comments are: "Ten little Indians, and then there were nine." . . . "Who'll be the next to go?" . . . "We'd better hang together or we'll hang separately." . . . "Why should we help you; you'll probably leave soon, too."

The closed group has been found to be an excellent training device for teachers, for personnel in hospitals, social agencies, and outpatient clinics. Doctors and nurses participating in such groups have cited their heightened awareness of the therapeutic possibilities inherent in the daily routine of the hospital. Their positive attitudes are often strengthened and their negative ones modified. They also frequently gain more knowledge of their own anxieties and defenses.

Open Groups

Open groups also have specific features which carry certain definite advantages and disadvantages:

(1) Such groups may, in theory, perpetuate themselves indefinitely. They are never dissolved. Members who complete their treatment or leave for various reasons are replaced.

(2) Changes may be made to achieve a composition that will facilitate therapeutic movement. Thus, patients may be added or transferred elsewhere at the therapist's discretion.

(3) Such groups may be started with only a few patients, with new members added from time to time to fulfill current needs.

Certain themes, especially the so-called birth theme, arise more readily in open than in closed groups. The kinds of anxieties and hostilities that emerged when a new baby was born, or a step-parent or grandparent entered the family circle, are re-experienced by patients at this time. "Killing off" this family-member prototype may even be acted out symbolically in the group. In fact, a new member may be literally ejected by the group unless the therapist is alert to this possibility and is prepared to analyze what happens.

Dora, a case in point, was a 28-year-old member of an outpatient group. Whenever a new male member joined, she would experience a slight breathing difficulty. However, when a woman two years her junior joined the group, Dora had an acute asthma attack during the session. At this point she recalled her younger sister's birth when she herself was 8 years old. The mother suffered an intense postpartum depression which forced Dora to assume complete care of the baby sister. She subsequently developed asthma which persisted for several years and was followed by a few more years of bronchial catarrh. This revelation and the ensuing discussion served to open the floodgates of memory for other members. For several weeks they discussed long-forgotten or "shelved" material related to their respective traumatic experiences when their families were enlarged.

The entrance of any newcomer must be carefully timed because of its possible disruptive effect. The inevitable increase of anxiety among the group members will be reflected in the sessions, and will either facilitate or hinder communication. A newcomer can provide stimulation when the group is in a stagnant period. However, this provocation would be most unwise if the whole group were in a resistance phase calling for analysis of the transference factors involved. Ideally, the therapist should be able to predict the group's reaction more or less accurately. Different group climates are certain to elicit quite different communication patterns in response to a new member. But in most instances the emergence of unconscious material and underlying conflicts is impeded by the presence of the stranger, regardless of the current stage of treatment.

Individual group members' reactions to a newcomer vary. Some ignore him; others engage in overt and/or covert moves to exclude him from participation. Some seek to be very friendly; thus they may attack the therapist directly for having foisted a new sibling on them.

The reactions of the new member to this cold or even hostile reception are likely to be mediated by his natural need for acceptance. In order to merge quickly into the group—instead of remaining an outsider—he usually accepts its patterns unquestioningly and conforms to what he considers to be its values and its needs. Fortunately, group "veterans" can and do help a new member become acclimatized and absorbed into the group therapy relationship, after they have faced and started to work through their earlier conflicts over the birth of a real sibling.

Separation anxiety is also found in open groups, but to a lesser extent than in closed groups. Even so, patients use various tactics to hold on to members: "Don't go; you understand me and I like you." . . . "You're too sick to leave." However, some patients accept and encourage departure. One member said, "I'm glad *someone's* well enough to go. Maybe one of these days it will be me."

Four Basic Types of Communication

A desideratum in all life relationships is effective communication. The four basic types of communication in a group can be described in geometric terms[3]. At one extreme is *vertical* communication, and at the other, *horizontal;* in between lie *triangular* and *circular* communication. All foster very different climates. Their unique qualities are summarized in Table 1.

The therapist's personality, value system[4], and conception of his role enter into his preference for, and skill in using, one type of communication or another. If he relies largely on vertical or triangular communication, his groups will tend to be *therapist-centered*[5]. If he encourages horizontal communication, his groups will tend to be *authority-denying*[6]. And if he believes circular communication best furthers therapeutic progress, his groups will tend to be *group-centered.*

In *therapist-centered* groups, the therapist considers himself the focus and believes that no reconstruction of personality can take place unless he is present. He assumes that only original parental transference neurosis leads to such reconstruction and that multiple transferences are merely derivative. All material must therefore be channeled through him; the group is used to elicit interaction phenomena which are worked through in subsequent individual sessions.

Communication in therapist-centered groups is usually either vertical or triangular. Vertical communication may be described as one-way communication between a definite and recognized authority prototype and the patient toward whom this expert knowledge is directed at the moment. In triangular communication, the therapist is at the apex of the triangle, channeling and controlling member-to-member communication, giving interpretations, limiting the patients' intragroup and extragroup activities.

In *authority-denying* groups, the therapist not only repudiates the role of expert authority but brings to the group his own aches, discomforts, frustrations, conflicts, dreams, and other personal manifestations. He expects the members to help him cope with his problems, just as he helps them cope with theirs. "The group can grow only if I grow with them." This kind of mutual therapeutic aid is considered the group's cardinal purpose. Affect arousal is regarded as the motor that produces healthful change. Horizontal communication is characteristic of such groups. It may be mentioned that a number of professionals in the field believe it is impossible to achieve true status equalization in therapy groups. Furthermore, the therapist's stated desire to be "just another member" is somewhat contradicted by his acceptance of fees.

In *group-centered groups,* the therapist does not deny his authority role but considers himself in the role of an expert participant. He takes for granted the group's inherent maturational and "curative" properties. The group is used to modify transference and countertransference phenomena. Multiple transferences, both sibling and parental, are of the utmost importance. Individual sessions are kept to a minimum and the need for them is usually related to resistance to

TABLE 1. Qualities of Four Different Types of Group Communication

UNDERLYING PHILOSOPHICAL PRINCIPLES	VERTICAL	TRIANGULAR
I. EXPERTNESS	Only the therapist can effect change. Change within the individual limited.	Only the therapist can effect changes. Change within the individual limited.
II. ROLE OF THE THERAPIST AND THE GROUP	Group is auxiliary. Elevation of one person and devaluation of group autonomy. Hierarchical position of therapist.	Group can function only under defined and controlled leadership of the therapist.
III. SIGNIFICANCE OF STATUS	The confronted patient works through his conflict only with constant help of titular authority.	The confronted patient works through his conflict only with constant help of titular authority.
IV. VALUE PLACED ON RELATIONSHIP BY GROUP MEMBERS	One-to-one static authoritative therapist-patient relationship or authorized group relationship.	Variability of relationship is limited to the therapeutic milieu determined by therapist.
V. VALUE PLACED ON DIFFERENT KINDS OF SYMBOLS AND ON REAL EXPERIENCE	Importance of therapeutic structure. Stress on symbolic transference and not on aspects of immediate experience.	Importance of therapeutic structure. Stress on transference and not on immediate experience.
VI. RELATIONSHIP BETWEEN IMPULSE AND CONTROL	Irrational impulses suppressed and controlled.	Emerging impulse wish must be understood and controlled.

TABLE 1. (*Continued*)

UNDERLYING PHILOSOPHICAL PRINCIPLES	HORIZONTAL	CIRCULAR
I. EXPERTNESS	Complete equalization.	Recognition of the therapist as functional expert but therapeutic group leadership fostered.
II. ROLE OF THE THERAPIST AND THE GROUP	All leadership structure considered undesirable for growth processes.	Therapist's guidance leads to ever-growing and rotating group leadership.
III. SIGNIFICANCE OF STATUS	Both functional and titular status denied.	Patients initially seek titular status, then learn to discriminate between titular and functional status.
IV. VALUE PLACED ON RELATIONSHIP BY GROUP NUMBERS	Structured relationship considered limiting to growth.	Tolerance of various and variable positive and negative relationships among group members. Therapist's role to raise the level of all peers toward equalization of status.
V. VALUE PLACED ON DIFFERENT KINDS OF SYMBOLS AND ON REAL EXPERIENCE	Importance of direct experience stressed.	Emphasis on importance of confrontation with transference relationships. Reliving stressed.
VI. RELATIONSHIP BETWEEN IMPULSE AND CONTROL	Impulse must rule= reason hinders growth.	Emerging impulse wish must be understood and may be acted upon, as the situation requires.

the group process by either patient or therapist or both of them.

Circular communication is the salient feature of group-centered therapy. The therapist's authority is at all times a functional one. His premise is that the group's social climate carries the potential for equal participation and reciprocal response by all members. In the ensuing multiple transferences, peer and parental relationships are considered of equal importance. If the therapist is thoroughly familiar with the diagnostic and emotional involvements of the members, he can tolerate a considerable amount of anxiety while helping them avoid possible pitfalls. By encouraging rotating leadership, he helps to foster a climate characterized by equality and interdependence of individuals in the group. This form of communication stimulates both antagonistic and positive emotions; relationships are continually broken and restored and new ones are formed.

The likelihood of a patient's changing his life patterns constructively is increased with the breadth and intensity of his relationships with a variety of persons—sibling as well as parental prototypes. The group, a natural setting of all human affiliations, may provoke endless conflicts similar to those encountered by the patient in his life experiences on the outside.

This is well illustrated by the case of Leonard, a 29-year-old engineer. Martha, a solidly built, matter-of-fact group member had become for him the image of his older sister, while petite and fragile Sophie became his younger sister. He fought constantly with Martha and accused her, among other things, of ingratiating herself with the therapist who was a mother prototype. Extremely protective and warm toward Sophie, he was suddenly shocked to discover a closeness developing between her and Martin.

Martin was Leonard's ideal of manhood—virile-looking, practical, intellectually keen and successful in business. He also had a toolchest like one owned by Leonard's father. Leonard thus re-experienced his failure in an earlier rivalry relationship with his father. He came to understand his feelings toward the original family situation by reliving it in the group, experiencing numerous changes in his relationships during successive meetings. His reactions to Sophie and to the therapist were continually redefined and altered as a result of his strong reaction to Sophie's attachment to Martin and the therapist.

Combined or Conjoint Therapy

When a patient meets in a group and also individually with the same therapist, this is known as combined therapy. It is proposed that the term *conjoint therapy* be used to describe individual and group treatment for the same patient with different therapists.

In individual psychotherapy the dyadic relationship is hierarchical, whether the patient is on a couch or facing the therapist. This relationship fosters dual transferences, though multiple transferences may be fantasied. Emphasis is primarily on intrapsychic processes. Conflicts are centered largely around parental prototype figures, and dependency elements are paramount.

A number of therapists who use combined treatment rely mainly on the one-to-one relationship for working through primary separation anxiety, manifold resistances, and parental transference manifestations. Individual sessions are then the main therapeutic focus with the group merely an adjunct. In any event, when the combined approach is used, the group is usually regarded as a bridge to individual sessions or, conversely, individual sessions as a bridge to the group[7].

However, some therapists have found merit in another type—*concurrent therapy*—in which the therapist conceives of group and individual treatment as true parallels, with no bridge between them[8]. Proponents of this form say they neither emphasize nor favor one or the other form of treatment. "Therapy takes on new dimensions: It is rather like seeing a sphere from all sides and from within at the same time, as well as perceiving its relationship to the world around it"[9]. Lipshutz[10] and Bieber[11] cite the value of these parallel sessions for a more complete working through of problems on various psychological and developmental levels.

Both intrapsychic and interpersonal processes may be observed in group as well as individual therapy settings. Some therapists hold that the group offers a wider scope for tolerance and identification than is possible in a one-to-one relationship. A review of the literature substantiates the view that group therapy may be regarded as the treatment of choice for many patients and, combined with some individual therapy, for most patients. It is not an inferior approximation of individual therapy but a treatment method with unique characteristics.

It may be well to mention a pitfall of all forms of combined therapy. Patients tend to sort out and withhold material instead of offering it spontaneously when it comes to mind—a primary principle in all therapy. For example, a woman told her male therapist, "I had a strange dream and saved it for our sessions together." Another said, "At the last group meeting I had a fantasy that everyone disappeared, leaving you and me alone in the room." A man working with a female therapist said, "I feel wonderful. The whole group is angry and forbidding just like my father. But they don't know I'm really mama's favorite and we play together when they're not around." Each of these remarks revealed that the group had been completely excluded in favor of the therapist. "I'm saving my treats for you; I don't want the group to know how close we are to each other." The extent of a patient's saving of material for either group or individual sessions is almost never clear to him because it is unconscious. The therapist can be especially alert for material which is presented differently by the patient in individual and in group sessions.

Coordinated Meetings

The term *coordinated meetings* has been suggested to cover three types of regularly scheduled meetings comprising all members of a psychotherapy group except the therapist[12]. Known as alternate, premeetings, and postmeetings, they are interspersed with the regular group meetings at which the therapist is present.

Alternate meetings were introduced by Wolf to "legitimatize" and bring within the framework of group psychotherapy the inevitable spontaneous gatherings taking place after regular group sessions[13]. Aware that such get-togethers pointed up the patients' need to let off steam, explore their feelings further, and lessen their anxieties, he made them an accepted feature of group treatment. Once these sessions are initiated in a group, all members are required to participate.

Alternate meetings usually take place in members' homes more or less in rotation[14, 15]. If the home of one patient is preferred, because of its central location for example, he may come to resent the responsibility. When a member's office is available, it is sometimes preferable to a home because it is less personal. Members often arrange for light refreshments. Alcoholic drinks are almost always suggested and usually tried. However, after one experience with alcoholic beverages, the members are usually against such experimentation. The equilibrium of the group may be threatened by alcohol.

Postmeetings, which immediately follow regular sessions, are held in the therapist's office in his absence, a member's home, or a nearby eating place. This kind of meeting is often regarded as the cradle of the alternate meeting.

Premeetings, held in the therapist's office just before regular group sessions, are closest within his orbit. Because he is expected momentarily, there is not as noticeable a release in tension as in the other two types of coordinated meetings. Members exhibit "good" behavior and all-around conformity as they vie strongly for the therapist's approval. This meeting has been found a valuable "warm-up" before regular meetings in institutional settings (*e.g.* Veterans' Administration hospitals) and various clinics.

The therapist is advised not to initiate coordinated meetings until the group has weathered many ups and downs during regular sessions with him, or until the ego strength of the members is sufficient to restrain destructive forms of acting out.

Spontaneous social gatherings of two or more members, so-called subgroups or splinter-groups, should be strongly discouraged. Some therapists expressly forbid them because they are conducive to acting out transference resistances[16, 17]. In some instances activities of such subgroups have threatened the group's equilibrium and sometimes even its very existence. When meetings of subgroups of two or more members come to the therapist's attention, as they are bound to do, he will have a good opportunity to bring up the subject of coordinated meetings, explaining that emotions engendered among members must be analyzed by him and by the group itself. The subject may be introduced in this way:

"You seem to have lots of things to say, more than we have time for here. How would you like to meet once a week, without me, at each other's home?" Objections from members who need the therapist's protection, whatever their expressed reasons, usually run along these lines: "What good would that do?" . . . "They're just as dumb as I am." . . . "I'm seeing too much of those squares already." . . . "Jane will try to run everything, if you're not here." . . . "It won't be a meeting; it'll be a shambles."

It must be noted that while many patients tend to probe for and reveal previously suppressed feelings when alone with their peers, other patients' conflicts and difficulties become more pronounced. These individuals feel "safer" and are more communicative when the therapist is present and are likely to develop endless excuses for non-attendance at coordinated meetings.

In order to lessen the heightened anxiety of the group, the therapist could emphasize that he is not casting the group members adrift but is placing a good deal of confidence in them. Such reassurance may be necessary because so many patients seeking psychotherapy feel helpless, lonely, and mistrustful of their own judgment, regardless of their professed complaint.

The first coordinated meeting will require careful planning. If the majority agree to meet on their own, the reluctance of a few members usually can be overcome. Some groups even draw up a few simple rules governing the time limit of their meeting, refreshments, and the like.

All coordinated meetings represent a mediating step toward the patient's utilization of his affective resources without bolstering by an "omnipotent" parental prototype. In the group-member's individual development, the alternate meeting is analogous to the peer group outside his home, while regular meetings are experienced as his early home milieu. In the home, as in regular sessions, the children—patients vie for acceptance by the parental figure—the therapist.

Peer-group meetings tend to have a much more fluid organization than regular meetings. Though still in the shadow of the parental orbit, the group members escape it briefly. Just as children tend to share with their peers their complaints or strongly positive feelings about others, so do patients who meet on their own tend to air their hostile or warm feelings. Group solidarity is also fostered in this climate: patients begin to think in terms of "We feel, think, want . . ." rather than "The therapist thinks, feels, wants . . ."

Coordinated meetings offer another means of facilitating communication that will point up the patients' flawed interpersonal relationships. Among his peers, each member tends to view his present behavior against the backdrop of his earlier experiences. With increased understanding of his own personality, he can begin to incorporate this newly found knowledge into his life situation.

In reconstructive therapy the individual must first come to recognize his own feelings, attitudes, and value system, how they originated and how they influence his present behavior. Then he can attempt to modify these elements. Only when they are modified can interpersonal relationships be altered. Learning to consolidate his discrimination between past and present relationships (working through) aids him in affecting a separation from parental dependency in its many forms. Participation in concerted group action enables the patient to assume a responsible role at a critical time—when another member needs support or threatens the group's equilibrium. This giving and receiving of protection is probably the strongest single element in growth and maturation.

Leadership emerges and changes readily in coordinated meetings. As patients progress in therapy, they relinquish their intense dependency on the therapist. Nonparticipants who are used to "leaning" on others begin to rely more and more on their own resources. Formerly active members seek support in return for support given. To cite an example, John sat quietly through most of a group session when another member said, "What's the matter with you? You've hardly let out a peep." John replied, "I've worked hard enough to help you; now I'm in a slump and it's your turn to help me."

Coordinated meetings also foster shifts in perception, meaningful personal experiences, and tolerance for affective outbursts. With help from the others, members come to recognize discrepancies between their behavior patterns in coordinated and in regular sessions and begin to probe for the reasons underlying these differences. Ernest was attacked by the group in a hostile manner because of his silence in the regular session. After some time, and with help from his peers, he became aware that his hostile feelings toward the therapist actually prevented him from communicating in her presence.

On the other hand, some patients who are shy and withdrawn at regular meetings, may become aggressive and boisterous when the therapist is absent. This is particularly true of those with passive-dependent traits. They may be seizing their first opportunity to explore assertive feelings previously denied. It is likely that ego building proceeds in the therapist's intermittent absence. After learning to give and withhold affective experiences, patients gradually incorporate authority and autonomy—the essence of ego-building activity.

In coordinated meetings where communication is horizontal or circular, destructive acting out for purposes of challenging or besting the authority figure may be directed toward the therapist or group members. Close physical proximity and other factors in this setting can engender various forms of acting out: aggressive (physical threats), regressive (childlike behavior), or sexual maneuvers[16-18]. These manifestations may threaten the therapist's security and value system as well as the group's equilibrium[19]. If the acting out is not brought up by the members the therapist will have to introduce the issue so that it can be discussed and analyzed as soon as possible. He may then suggest individual sessions for the persons involved.

How does the therapist learn of what has happened in coordinated meetings? In general, members report their reactions to the events taking place there. After checking each report, and noting verbal, nonverbal, and anxiety clues, the therapist usually has a good grasp of the interactions and precipitating causes. Thus, most of the material arising in such sessions can be related to, and analyzed within, the framework of regular sessions. Deliberate withholding of vital material must, of course, be analyzed.

If a splinter group or the whole group decides to hold out, one of the eight to ten members is likely to leak information—to lessen his own guilt or to "get in good" with the authority figure. Such disclosures, significant in themselves, often reveal much about the tale-bearer. It is important to make members aware of the importance of bringing any and all essential material for analysis by the therapist and the group. At the start of each regular session, the therapist may ask whether anyone would like to discuss his thoughts and feelings from the alternate meeting, as one way of making explicit the close alliance between the two kinds of sessions.

Institution of coordinated meetings may arouse some anxiety in the therapist. Since many subtle and obvious factors are involved when he encourages group members to meet on their own, he must analyze his conscious and unconscious attitudes and feelings toward the whole question of such meetings.

How much aggression and regression can the therapist tolerate without intervening, without being forbidding and punitive? Will he be unduly disturbed if the group's value system conflicts with his own? Can he tolerate being excluded from their confidence at times? Can he stand being directly challenged? He should try to answer these questions as honestly as he can.

Coordinated meetings should not be initiated by a therapist who believes that: (*1*) his own authority is all important; (*2*) the group structure, with himself as focus, is immutable; (*3*) any acting out is destructive and must be suppressed; (*4*) complete control is desirable at all times.

The therapist's need to protect his "children" by holding onto them has been underestimated. However, children do eventually leave home, and coordinated meetings may help to cushion the leave-taking for both patients and therapist. It is better not to start these meetings at all, if there is a possibility of having to discontinue them midway. This move would reinforce the patients' early experiences with interfering and/or punitive parents. As one young man said, "My parents let me use the car but the first time I got home after midnight, they said, 'No more car for you.'"

The clearer the therapist's concept of his role, the easier he will find it to cope with difficult situations in the group. When with one patient, that patient is of course his principal concern. But when with a group, the entire group must be all-important. As he becomes increasingly concerned with its problems and activities and feels more at ease with all members, the need for individual sessions to prevent destructive acting out or to deal with its consequences will steadily diminish.

References

1. KADIS, A. L., Re-experiencing the family constellation in group psychotherapy. *Am. J. Individ. Psychol.* 12:63, 1956.
2. KADIS, A. L., Analytic group work with teachers. *J. Nat. Assoc. Women Deans & Counselors.* 23, 2:78, 1960.
3. KADIS, A. L., The philosophy of group therapy. Paper read at Postgraduate Center for Psychotherapy, 1959.
4. PAPANEK, H., Change of ethical values in group psychotherapy. *Internat. J. Group Psychotherapy* 4:435, 1958.
5. WOLF, A., and SCHWARTZ, E. K., Psychoanalysis in groups: three primary parameters. *Am. Imago* 14:281, 1957.
6. MULLAN, H., Status denial in group psychoanalysis. *J. Nerv. & Ment. Diseases,* 122:345, 1955.
7. KADIS, A. L., and MARKOWITZ, M., "Group Psychotherapy," in D. Brower, L. Abt (eds.), *Progress in Clinical Psychology,* Vol. 3. New York, Grune & Stratton, 1958, p. 154.

8. SAGER, C. J., The effects of group therapy on individual psychoanalysis. *Internat. J. Group Psychotherapy* 4:403, 1959.
9. Ibid.
10. LIPSHUTZ, D. M., Combined group and individual psychotherapy. *Am. J. Psychotherapy* 11:336, 1957.
11. BIEBER, T. B., The emphasis on the individual in psychoanalytic group therapy. *Internat. J. Social Psychiatry* 2:275, 1957.
12. KADIS, A. L., The role of co-ordinated group meetings in group psychotherapy. *Acta Psychotherapeutica Psychosomatica et Orthopaedagogica* 7:Suppl., 174, 1959.
13. WOLF, A., and SCHWARTZ, E. K., Psychoanalysis in groups: the alternate session. *Am. Imago* 17:101, 1960.
14. KADIS, A. L., The alternate meeting in group psychotherapy. *Am. J. Psychotherapy* 10:275, 1956.
15. KADIS, A. L., "Alternate Meetings," *Topical Problems of Psychotherapy*, Vol. 2. p. 164. Basel, Karger, 1960.
16. DURKIN, H., GLATZER, H. T., KADIS, A. L., WOLF, A., and HULSE, W. C., Acting out in group psychotherapy: a panel discussion. *Am. J. Psychotherapy* 12:87, 1958.
17. SLAVSON, S. R., The nature and treatment of acting out in group psychotherapy. *Internat. J. Group Psychotherapy* 1:3, 1956.
18. WOLF, A., BROSS, R., FLOWERMAN, S., GREENE, J. S., KADIS, A. L., LEOPOLD, H., LOCKE, N., MILBERG, I. J., MULLAN, H., OBERS, S. J., and ROSENBAUM, M., Sexual acting out in the psychoanalysis of groups. *Internat. J. Group Psychotherapy* 4:369, 1954.
19. WOLF, A., Psychoanalysis in groups. *Am. J. Psychotherapy* 3:525, 1949; 4:16, 1959.

dreams 9

In the dream, we re-experience the past,
forget the present
and foretell the future—STEKEL.[1]

PROGRESS in group psychotherapy, as in individual psychoanalysis, owes much to the study of dreams. They offer one of the best means of delving with the now and beyond the here and now. Dreams provide the key to what may be a veritable Pandora's box. The patient who reports a dream may be aided not only by the therapist but also by his peers in becoming aware of the thoughts, feelings, fantasies, and hopes lurking within the dream. The group members' own associations are sometimes able to break through the dreamer's blockings and reluctance to penetrate the significance of his dream.

Patients are likely to tell their dreams in all types of psychotherapy groups, whether in a clinical setting or in private practice. Dreams are also reported in counseling and guidance groups. Regardless of the therapist's philosophy and orientation, he will have to respond in some way to the intimate message which dreams convey. It is therefore most important for the therapist to have sufficient knowledge of dreams to deal with them in a way that best meets the patient's needs at his particular phase of therapy and in his particular group setting. The therapist will find that patients are very sensitive to his reaction to their dream material. A patient whose dreams are regularly ignored may withdraw from participation in the group or even from the group.

What Are Dreams?

It is well known that all biologic processes are constantly geared to maintain or restore a state of equilibrium, in order to prevent dysfunction or even disintegration of the organism. Since dreams are biological phenomena, they follow this principle of balance. Like all other human functions, dreams maintain their role as part of the human body's protective, defensive, and regulatory apparatus. Recent research has suggested that an appropriate amount of "dream time" each night is desirable and perhaps necessary.

Dreams may be called precursors of conscious thought. They represent an undeveloped or embryonic phase of thinking. Occurring as they do in the borderland between the unconscious and the conscious, the so-called preconscious, they furnish invaluable clues to thought evolution and to various disturbances of the human mind. These disturbances may be viewed as conflicts between the individual's conscious and unconscious self.

Beneficial Effects of Dreams

Dreams are in the service of the individual's adaptation and, thus, of his survival. In each individual's life, dreams have specific functions: (*1*) They protect the integrity of his ego and safeguard the continuity of his mental existence. (*2*) They regulate the flow of his emotions and thus help to maintain his mental equilibrium. (*3*) They protect his sleep, so necessary to "recharge his batteries" for another day. (*4*) They act as an agency of wish-fulfillment, meeting many instinctual needs, such as unbridled sexual desires that are usually frustrated by the individual's moral censorship[2]. (*5*) They may be nature's way of protecting not only our equilibrium but also our sanity, according to recent research studies.

Adler emphasized the dream's teleological aspects. He perceived the dream as an expression of the dreamer's total personality and lifestyle, as well as having problem-solving functions—"training for tomorrow"[3]. The dream mirrors the dreamer's total personality and is intimately interwoven with his waking everyday life.

Dreams serve as a means of discharging emotional energy, and thus relieve many of our emotional pressures. For example, an employee may feel like hitting his overbearing boss, but he does not act on this impulse because he needs his job. By dreaming, he can discharge his accumulated resentment without any harmful consequences but rather with beneficial emotional effects. He may awaken in a more pleasant mood, with self-respect restored and tension lessened, savoring the triumph of a "good deed well done." Considering all the internal and external pressures to which one is regularly exposed, it would be difficult to overestimate the value of the mighty safety valve of dreams.

Dreams also play an important role by lessening the shock of certain experiences that might injure the ego[4]. Repeated dreams of certain dreaded events—loss of a beloved person, loss of a job, failure to pass an examination, and so on—make them lose part of their traumatizing potential. Following the law of diminishing returns, the shock of a distressing happening is gradually attenuated until the experience becomes routine. For example, a young woman in a therapy group was strongly attached to her father, who was suffering from a fatal disease. She repeatedly dreamed that he had died and she felt real grief in her dreams. By re-experiencing this tragic event again and again in dreams, she gradually became somewhat "immunized." When her father actually died, the impact of her loss was softened because the repetition had cushioned her pain.

All forms of analytic therapy stress the discovery and understanding of facets of the personality not commonly at the disposal of the conscious. Analytic therapy is essentially concerned with revealing unconscious motivations and goals, as well as dynamic connections. Dreams are always psychological expressions of deeper emotions and conflicts. The dreamer is related to this current conflict and to its possible future solution. The current conflict also represents conflicts in his earlier life. His dream carries the thread of all the emotional problems in his life history and also in the therapeutic situation. The dream merges the past, the present, and the future.

In group psychotherapy, the understanding of the dream not only may further the dreamer's progress but it is likely to be important for the entire group. The group or the individual members are represented in each other's dream[5,6]. In fact, the extent to which other members enter his dream picture reveals the degree to which the dreamer has developed group "relatedness." A male member who entered a group after a considerable period in individual treatment said: "This is funny. I used to have lots of dreams where I was the pilot and fell from my plane. Last night I dreamed I was poised on a diving board and lots of people were watching. I didn't dare dive in for fear of breaking my neck. It was bad enough to crash from a plane by my-myself, but now I have *you* around to watch me break my neck."

Some Techniques for Dealing with Dreams

How may dreams reported in a group be used to further therapeutic movement? The therapist may encourage the patient to associate to a dream in its entirety as well as to its details. "Did you have a dream since our last session?" or "Do you remember any dreams that have recurred often?" are questions that indicate the therapist's interest in communication media other than reality material. In both group and individual sessions he may ask, in response to dream material, "When did you have this dream? Do you have any thoughts about what it may mean to you? Did anything happen during the previous day that you can relate to the dream?" Or if a name has come up repeatedly in the dream, "What does the name Peter mean to you?" After the dreamer has given any relevant material that comes to mind, the group members may be asked to respond: "Do any of you have any reactions or associations to the dream or to any part of it? Is something in it so particularly meaningful that this might have been *your* dream?" It will be found that the therapist's role as dream interpreter diminishes as the group develops the capacity to explore unconscious material.

Sometimes it is helpful to let the patient associate each element of the dream as an aspect of himself. For example, a middle-aged man who was the oldest in his family related the following: "There wasn't any sequence to my dream last night. There was just a big bed in it, and that's all I remember." When the therapist asked, "What part of yourself do you think of as the bed?" he replied quickly, "All of me; everybody used me as featherbedding. All my business partners are relatives. I feel as if they all lean or lie on top of me." Then he added resentfully, "But even a bed gets worn out, and I'm getting worn out too."

It is important for the therapist to attempt to grasp the dream's specific messages for him as fully as possible. He is not obligated to interpret or divulge these messages; the dreamer will consider his questioning an acceptable response.

In a group analytic setting, the therapist uses all dreams that are brought up and spends as much time on each as seems advisable. A group poses a situation in which there is much ground to be covered because of the many persons who may be struggling for attention. Therefore, the therapist must be aware of the need to use techniques which prevent dreams from getting "lost." This is particularly important early in the group's life. Relating a dream produces anxieties, mobilizes resistances, and reinforces defenses in the dreamer and in other group members for whom it carries a special meaning. The therapist must, of course, deal with these anxieties, resistances, and defenses in all members of a group. At times, the dreamer's resistance to understanding his dream is broken down by the associations of other members. When the dream evokes real anxiety in a group member, he usually tries to divert attention from the basic issues being discussed.

A woman in a therapy group had always blocked any association to her dream material. In relating a dream, she said, "I was riding on a Third Avenue *El* train plainly marked with the letter *L*." She associated to this dream by saying, "The *El* is, of course, being torn down; I watched the workmen breaking up tracks yesterday." Unwilling to accept this simple explanation, a member asked, "Why were you riding the *El* anyway? Was this your usual transportation?" She said she had never been on the *El* in her life, but kept insisting that she'd often thought of the passing of this landmark. "What does the letter *L* mean to you? What is its significance? Are we the workmen, breaking up your defenses?" another member asked. After thinking this over, the woman said, "You wouldn't know this, but my maiden name was *L——*, and I've always used it professionally. No one at business even knows my married name. I wonder if this means I'm at last ready to stop being a member of the *L——* family and really set up a family unit with my husband. Is my resistance to bearing my husband's name being broken down, as the *El* is being broken down?" It was the first time she had recognized this present emotional conflict which was revealed by a symbol of dependence from the past, the *L* of her maiden name. She might not have been aware of the conflict at the moment if her peers hadn't probed for the meaning of this symbol. During the exchange of associations many other members explored the universal theme of dependency, both passive and hostile.

In this instance, group members effectively coped with the dreamer's resistance. A number of group therapists have reported that patients who had special difficulties with dreams while in individual analysis began to experience meaningful dreams when in a group. If the group member cannot recall his own dreams he may be able to mirror himself and his problems, his present and past, in the dream of another group member. A unique quality in the group dream is each member's projection as he responds to the dream of another group member. We often hear a patient say, "John, this is my dream. I don't believe what you say about my dream. You're talking about your problem and not mine." John will often answer, "You are right. It is truly my problem."

At times, however, the group members' resistance to the therapist or to the dreamer makes them unwilling to respond to the dream. Instead they try to ward off further discussion by insisting on relating their own dreams or changing the subject abruptly. The therapist must recognize this as a transference-resistance factor, and help the group to explore it fully. When the therapist asks the group: "What makes you reluctant to respond to this dream?" the answer may have many implications, among them angry feelings toward the therapist and/or the dreamer: "We don't want to help him."

Means of Overcoming Resistance

In dealing with resistance manifestations, it may be well to examine some of the maneuvers a dreamer uses to make light of or to disown his dreams. Many patients insist that they don't dream or, if they dream, they don't remember anything on awakening. Others give only fragments of a dream. Some tend to minimize its importance and may at the same time discount any possible help forthcoming from the group. The majority of patients initially state that they don't understand any part of their dreams.

The therapist will find many clues in the patient's manner of relating a dream and timing the account. The patient may purposely, although unconsciously, tell his dream to one person only, either the therapist or a group member. He may look at him while excluding the other group members. Or he may tell the dream to the entire group without looking at anyone. He may tell the dream because one person is not present at the time. In groups that have alternate meetings or have combined therapy, the dreamer often carries his exclusion practices even further. He may relate his dream only when he is alone with the therapist, only in an alternate meeting, or in a regular meeting, sometimes only after having told it to the therapist. Some patients may not present any dreams at all.

It is always appropriate for the therapist to say, "Why do you tell your dream only to me, or to Jane?" or "You haven't related a dream for a long while. Are you telling this one because Jack is absent?" Pointing out such discrepancies helps to focus attention on dream elements that are not readily apparent, so the patients can work with them.

Two examples show how dreams elicit free associations by the dreamer and other members which help to overcome the dreamer's initial reluctance to "own" his dream and help work with it on many levels.

One member in a group related the following dream: "I was riding and riding in the subway, apparently not going anywhere. That's all. I ride the subway almost every day so why should I dream about it? It's silly. Maybe the word has some different meaning." A woman member said, "Sub-way, under-ground—a woman is under a man; I think of the sub-conscious too." The dreamer replied: "I didn't think of that. Maybe it means I can 'go under' now. I've never dared to deal with my subconscious." Another member chimed in: "For me the idea of going under—under water, under a woman, into my subconscious— is very, very threatening." From this point, various new members started to reveal and deal with their problems on a "subway" level.

In another group, a woman brought up the following: "I had a strange dream in which I was determined to sue someone. I went to a lawyer about it though I knew, even in the dream, that if I won the case I'd lose in the long run." Then with a laugh she continued: "I don't want to sue anyone. I can't imagine why I had such a dream." An old member asked: "Who is Sue?" To which she hastily replied: "I don't know." He said: "Then why did you answer so quickly, without even thinking?" After a pause, she said: "I had completely forgotten, but I have a casual friend named Sue whose husband is a very successful artist. I guess I must identify myself with her. If I were Sue, I wouldn't have to sue my husband because he isn't successful."

Some therapists, among them Klein-Lipshutz, believe the dreamer's resistances are more quickly loosened if the other members' associations are given first[7]. One disadvantage of this method is that the dreamer's associations may be colored by what he has heard, or side-tracked altogether.

Mullan believes that associations of group members to a dream destroy its nonteleological aspects[8]. "The latent dream, which is entirely non-teleological, is thought to be the reality of the individual's existence."

Dreams are rooted in universal problems and conflicts—*e.g.* those involving birth, death, and sex and the members' different experiencing of these basic problems and conflicts helps the whole group. The multiplicity of associations to a particular dream tends to reveal the essence of the dreamer's problem, his present, past, and future reality, and the therapeutic situation with its multiple transference manifestations. Indeed, it touches on the essential conflicts of all members in myriad ways.

The following dream was related by the only Negro member of a therapy group. "I feel on top of the world; I think I'm ready to leave. I have asserted myself with my wife and with my boss. But a dream I had recently bothers me. I was on the ground and a man was hacking at me with a hatchet. Though terribly shocked I felt no pain. I whispered to a woman passing by, 'Help me,' but she ignored me. The same thing happened when a man passed by. Then another woman came up to me, saying, 'Come with me to the fourth floor (the office of the male therapist was on this floor) and I'll give you a drink.' I went with her."

One group member said, "You told us your father beat you up when you were very young and you didn't try to defend yourself. It was the same in your dream; you let your assailant hack away at you without hitting back." Other comments were: "You said at first that you want to leave. Baloney. You're insulated against pain; that's why you didn't feel the cuts." . . . "Last time you said you wouldn't take any more guff from us. Are you running away because you're afraid we'll retaliate?" . . . "I wonder who the good samaritan woman is; can she be Dr. P——? Do you see him as a woman? Didn't you tell us your grandmother used to take care of you tenderly and give you milk to drink?" These various reactions actually dealt with the dreamer's defense mechanisms.

The therapist, aware that this patient's brittle defenses might make him leave the group or go into a depression, said: "I'm glad you're so much stronger now than you were. You didn't wake up in a panic and forget your dream; you remembered it clearly and brought it here so we could figuratively 'give you a drink' to help you." The patient's ego strength and defenses were evaluated and used for his support. It was established that his identification and transference to the therapist were linked with his grandmother. The members brought up his aggression at the previous session. They pointed out that even though he denied any fear, he *was* afraid of retaliation because of this outburst. Though he denied that they could cause him pain, he was probably supersensitive to their responses. They were able to identify with him—in feeling hacked at, paralayzed by the attack and unable to defend himself.

Multiple associations to the dreams of other members often make it easier for the dreamer to reveal the core of his problems. One patient recounted a dream in which he was on a float. Instead of water below, there was a sea of feces. "I have no idea what it means," he said. "Why be surprised?" said another man. "You always think of yourself as shit, as a nobody going nowhere." At this point a woman said, "You told us, John, that you suffered from diarrhea for many years as a child. You were afraid to ask to go to the bathroom on the first day of school, so you shit in your pants, then worried that the teacher would discover this. She did—by using her nose. I guess you're still shitting in your pants." John, after a pause, replied, "You're right. I not only feel like shit but I take all of it that you and my family dish out."

In therapy groups, one dream or a part of it has meaning for several members; they translate it into their own symbolic language. Sometimes, just when reactions and interactions on the theme are well under way, a member may eagerly present a new problem. The therapist should ask what motives prompted him to change the subject.

When universal themes such as birth, death, and sex are introduced as part of a dream or in associations to it, some members will not enter the discussion. They often try to change the subject, either by injecting a crisis, asking irrelevant questions, or offering dreams of their own that require immediate attention. The therapist, aware that a patient who cannot yet face certain of his conflicts figuratively runs away, must use all his skill to hold members to the theme. Any diversions, even potentially significant ones, should be shelved. In a group of married couples, one husband had a dream which he associated with his homosexual conflicts. A few other husbands were able to join in the discussion, bringing up their own fantasies and childhood experimentation. One husband, who had had homosexual experiences as an adult, became truly frightened and said, "Do we have to talk about this in the group? Everyone has read Kinsey. I have a lot more on my mind right now." The therapist replied, "Please let the other things wait." Then she added, "I hope that you wives will be just as courageous as your husbands in bringing up all your fantasies and experimentation with your own sex." One woman related an experience she had had in high school and several others—relieved to have the subject brought out into the open—then expressed their feelings, fantasies, and fears.

The breaking off or interruption of discussions of dreams is inherent in the group situation. However, these factors do not hinder the associative process but aid the therapist as well as the group members in understanding the meaningfulness of the dream. In the group, the therapist and group members have ample time and opportunity to make use of their "third ear" and "third eye." They will be alerted not only to verbal but especially to nonverbal manifestations. Even the slightest postural or motor "give-away" from the moment the patient comes in the door or starts to tell a dream, will be noticed and brought up: patients may enter slinking or with bravado, dressed up or sloppy, well-groomed or unkempt. He may sit on the edge of a chair or slump in it. He may cross his legs or have them widely separated. Taut facial muscles, anxious eyes, and a false smile are nonverbal clues to inner states[9, 10]. These states can be anxiety held in check, concealed tension, aggression, or resistance to what is going on at the time.

For example, Joan, a married woman, entered the room with a sad countenance. Immediately, she began to relate a dream which seemingly had happy connotations. But her anxious smile and tautly crossed legs made it obvious that she was concealing something. A member questioned the mood of the dream: "If this was such a nice dream, why do you look so anxious?" Joan replied: "I am anxious. I had to come here today to tell the dream. The car broke down and it took me two hours to get here." Another patient said: "What happened yesterday that you haven't told us? What are you holding back?" At this point, Joan admitted that a man in her community had recently been making advances to her. He had phoned her the day before, declaring his love, and said he would call her daily until she agreed to an assignation with him. " 'Don't spread on the flattery so thickly,' I told him. 'I don't believe you anyway.' But I'm really afraid of succumbing, of letting myself be seduced. He's a tall man. Maybe the tall workers in my dream, lugging heavy bundles into my house, represent this man. He's throwing into my lap all the things I want and am frightened of. I didn't see this connection before." The group members' alertness in watching for motor expressions that may belie verbal ones, helped the patient to relate pertinent material that might have gone unchallenged at that moment.

The direction of movement which is part of nonverbal communication is extremely helpful in understanding the dreamer[11]. Is the patient sitting, walking, or lying still? Is something coming toward the patient or going away from him? Does he fall from a place or take off in one? Does he go around in circles searching for something or climb directly to the top of a mountain? Usually a group quickly grasps the meaning of this symbolic language, as shown by this comment from one member to another: "In your dreams you never walk straight. You're always zig-zagging and never find what you're after. If you try to walk a straight road for once, instead of being devious, you may get what you're looking for, and it won't take as much time as this useless backing and filling." This response actually relates not only to the dreamer's manifest difficulty but is really as well a decription of the total life style and/or life patterning of the dreamer.

This kind of response is an illustration of one way in which dreams may be used by patients. In this case, the patient reported a dream instead of a verbalization. A related use is to report a dream because the patient cannot tell what his feeling is in his own words. He may present the dream as a method of selective communication with different members of the group, as a function of the way in which he perceives them at a particular time. He may be presenting a dream as a form of resistance, and may not only be resisting dynamically but may be offering a dream instead of a current reality problem that is bothering him, because he thinks the therapist "likes" the dream. The dream is likely to be a manifestation of his struggle with his problem, in the form of a communication to the therapist, one or more special group members, or the whole group. The dream, for some patients, is the only medium by which they can express themselves artistically.

The time at which the dream is presented may be extremely important. Whether it is presented at the very beginning of a session or the end or the middle or whether the patient asked for permission to tell it or begins doing so without asking, may all be very significant factors in understanding the meaning of the dream. Whether the dream occurred the night before the session, the night after the session, a few days on either side of a session, are all possibly related to the significance of the dream. Whether the dream was forgotten and then recalled is also often important as a clue to the changing self-concept of the dreamer that permitted him to forget a dream on one occasion and remember it on another.

The therapist may acquire much very valuable information from dreams. Such information may deal with diagnostics, psychodynamics, defenses, ego strength, anxiety, self-concept, and transference to and perception of the therapist, specific group members, and the group as a whole. How the dreamer perceives the audience for the dream may be partially suggested by whether he seems to be addressing the group as a whole or specific members of the group, when he recounts it.

Just what the therapist decides to do with the dream depends on his impression of the kind of information that it contains. What he does with the dream also depends on the phase of treatment in which the individual and the group are at the time of reporting the dream. He must decide the extent to which the group members are ready to explore the kind of unconscious communication represented by a dream. Some therapists feel that the associations of other group members help to overcome resistance in the dreamer and in themselves. Some therapists find that dreams represent a unique method for confronting the patient with his defenses and his repetitive life patterns. Dreams represent an opportunity for a continual airing of different kinds of movements in the group, and of both destructive and healthy manifestations. The extent to which different members of the group become involved with the symbolic language of dreams or regard them as less meaningful than other things, provide valuable clues on how the patient is faring in the group therapy situation.

Certain administrative considerations are important in understanding the reported dream. Thus, the therapist must consider whether the patient telling the dream is in combined treatment in which there is emphasis on group process and group sharing. A patient in concomitant treatment is likely to keep his dreams separate, with certain dreams for the group and others for individual sessions. A patient in conjoint treatment with two different therapists, is likely to pose special problems because he may have presented the same dream in the other situation and be engaging in resistance behavior by seeking what the other therapist does with the dream. Whether a dream that is reported in two different situations is reported differently in each one is of continual concern to the therapist.

Counseling and Guidance Groups

The leader of a counseling or guidance group should focus his attention on the most important part of a dream—the part that reflects conscious feelings and attitudes, the total of the life patterning of the person, his manifest goals and defenses—and disregard all other elements or persons in the dream that belong in the area of the subconscious, or, in other words, the symbolic language of the subconscious. The goal of the therapist is to treat the material that is closest to the "I"; I am, I walk, I did, I was sitting and waiting, I always walk backwards in my dreams, etc. In sum, all elements and material that are closest to the self, to one's ego, to one's life—the here and how—which are only an expression of one's total life patterning as well as life goal, can be brought to the awareness of the dreamer and other group members.

It should be kept in mind that the principal goal of guidance groups is to alleviate each individual's anxiety while strengthening his ego via healthy relationships with other members and with the therapist[12]. The principal goal of counseling (individual or in groups) is to help the individual achieve a better adaptation to reality and to his life demands. In both these forms of treatment, emphasis is on preconscious and conscious elements—the patient's "I," self, ego, his doing or not doing, his acting or not acting. Unconscious elements are to a great extent disregarded. Guidance and counseling are mostly provided by a social agency consulted by the client because he has a concrete problem requiring concrete help involving his family, his marriage, his children, or his job; or a hospital dealing with inpatients and their relatives in a day or night hospital setting[13]. The agency's intake worker is the one who usually refers the client for counseling or guidance. The groups tend to be more or less homogeneous—all mothers, all fathers, all adolescents, all elderly persons, and so on.

In such settings the therapist tries to sail on a positive relationship. Feelings, both positive and negative, are channeled mainly to those persons with whom the patients must deal in their everyday lives outside of the group, and generally concern daily reality adjustment problems. The therapist does not ask for dream material but it is likely to be offered spontaneously. He should try to understand the dreams at both the manifest and latent levels. Considerable skill is needed to grasp the latent meaning in a dream so that it can be kept out of the discussion. Unless the group leaders are constantly alert, latent conflicts will arise that cannot be dealt with adequately in such settings (unless the patient involved is seen individually at the same time). In short, any dream that is brought up may be linked with the patient's reality world but its latent material is used only for this linkage. In this as in other group situations, the dreamer's ability to recall the dream is a function of his perception of the audience for his dream[14].

References

1. STEKEL, W., *The Interpretation of Dreams*. New York, Liveright, 1943.
2. FREUD, S., *Collected Papers*, Vol. 5. London, Hogarth Press and the Institute of Psycho-Analysis, 1953.
3. ANSBACHER, H., and ANSBACHER, R., *Individual Psychology of Alfred Adler*. New York, Basic, 1956.
4. GUTHEIL, E., *The Handbook of Dream Analysis*. New York, Liveright, 1951.
5. BETLHEIM, S., Uber die Bedeutung des Traumes in der Gruppentherapie. *Acta Psychotherapeutica Psychosomatica et Orthopaedagogica* 6:56, 1958.
6. LOCKE, N., The use of dreams in group psychoanalysis. *Am. J. Psychotherapy* 11:98, 1957.
7. KLEIN-LIPSHUTZ, E., Comparison of dreams in individual and group psychotherapy. *Internat. J. Group Psychotherapy* 2:143, 1953.
8. MULLAN, H., The nonteleological in dreams in group psychotherapy. *J. Hillside Hospital* 5:480, 1956.
9. BERGER, M. M., Nonverbal communications in group psychotherapy. *Internat. J. Group Psychotherapy* 2:161, 1958.
10. WINICK, C., and HOLT, H., Some external modalities of group psychotherapy and their dynamic significance. *Am. J. Psychotherapy* 15:56, 1961.

11. ANSBACHER, H., and ANSBACHER, R., *Individual Psychology of Alfred Adler.* New York, Basic, 1956.
12. GINOTT, H. G., Differential treatment groups in guidance, counseling, psychotherapy, and psychoanalysis. *Internat. J. Social Psychiatry 2:*231, 1957.
13. WILLNER, G., The use of dream interpretation in group psychotherapy in a State Hospital. *Psychiatric Quart. Suppl. 28:*228, 1954.
14. WINICK, C., and HOLT, H., Differential recall of the dream as a function of audience perception. *Psychoanalysis and Psychoanalyt. Rev. 49:*53, 1962.

coping with special categories 10
of clinical problems

GROUP psychotherapy is advantageous for a great many persons need-
ing and seeking help for emotional problems. However, the group
psychotherapist must remember that it is not a method of treatment
for every type of clinical condition or behavior pathology. The therapist may be confronted with a variety of situations which may create
problems not only in the selection of patients for group psychotherapy
but also in the therapeutic management of patients within the group
process. Problems may arise because of factors which the therapist
cannot control, such as the reactions of other group members to the
communication of a patient. The mixture of sexes in a group may create
anxiety-provoking excitation and situations leading to adverse community reactions. This is especially relevant in small communities.
Various clinical problems will be discussed below.

Although each clinical problem must be evaluated in terms of the
individual person and existing circumstances, there are a few questions
which the group therapist may ask himself. The answers may often be
used as a rule of thumb in the selection of a patient with any existing
or anticipated therapeutic management problem, *e.g.*, homosexuality,
addiction, speech disorder, or psychosomatic symptoms.

(1) Am I able and do I want to cope with this problem in the group?

(2) How will the other group members react to this person? Will

they block his psychotherapeutic movement? Will he block and prevent the continued therapeutic movement of the group?

(3) Am I able to make time available for individual sessions if the group provokes anxiety above the particular patient's tolerance level? Am I able to make available time for individual sessions if combined treatment is indicated?

(4) What are the possible legal repercussions resulting from acting out if this patient enters the group?

(5) What facilities are at my disposal if the patient's condition requires hospitalization or other forms of treatment, *e.g.*, physical, electric, and/or pharmacological?

The psychotherapist must remember that he may be held responsible for and has to prevent and protect against destructive provocation within his group. The patient, in the light of the presenting and anticipated symptoms and problems, must be acceptable to the therapist. If the patient is to be seen in an outpatient clinic or agency, he must also meet the criteria for admission to the particular institution. The therapist must also consider possible legal elements involved in accepting the particular patient for group psychotherapy as he would for any treatment.

An excellent example of a clinical problem embodying most of these factors is drug addiction[1-11]. A great number and perhaps the majority of psychotherapists are very reluctant to treat these persons. The drug addict is usually involved with some arm of the law, local or Federal. If the group therapist feels himself capable and is willing to work with the addict, is he also willing to assume the possible involvement with the police or narcotics agents? If the patient is to be seen in a clinic or agency, the policies of the institution must be carefully considered. There is also the question of whether the treatment of the addict is to be reported to the pertinent law enforcement agency. If withdrawal of drugs is desired and/or required, facilities for this procedure must also be known and available for referral purposes. The legal aspects of drug addiction are in the province of state laws and may vary from area to area. The group therapist must be prepared to become familiar with and understand the existing laws within his practice area. Once these factors are clarified, the possible problems which may arise with the drug addict in the group can then be considered.

Starting with the addict, it may be of value to examine some of the specific categoric problems which most frequently confront the group therapist and to explore possible methods of coping with them. In working with the drug addict, it is most important that there be liaison with appropriate medical authorities. The group therapist must differentiate between the marijuana smoker, heroin addict, morphine user, and barbiturate addict. Often there is the question of whether the addict will infect other members of the group by teaching them about narcotics. This is most rare. Within the experience of the writers, patients in a group have a tendency to view addiction as symptomatic of a basic personality problem—as one patient put it, "It's a compulsion or an escape, the same as my always getting sick whenever things don't go right for me." The major problem which arises with an addict in the group is the hostility provoked in others by his frequent absences and then coming to the session under the influence of drugs. Although other group members may view the addict's drug use as symptomatic, they tend to resent the disruption of therapeutic progress provoked by absences and/or the inaccessibility of the person under the influence of drugs.

One of the major conflicts within the addict is intense feelings of nonacceptance by others. If the group therapist is able to accept the addict as a person within the group, the other group members' attitudes also become one of acceptance rather than rejection. The negative reactions which may arise within the other group members during the session may be used by the therapist to emphasize and differentiate the individual and his behavior. Although the addict's behavior may be criticized, his attendance at the group sessions is tantamount to his acceptance as a person. Most often, at least one, and frequently more, members of the group sense and identify with the feelings of rejection and loneliness experienced by the addict. The resulting support and protectiveness tend to create a feeling of belonging and in turn, increase ego strength of the addict. Sometimes, the addict may fall asleep as a defense against anticipated intolerable anxiety.

The intense negative reactions by other group members may advantageously be used to point out how nonverbal behavior patterns are not the most effective means of communication and that verbalizing one's feelings offers an opportunity to explore the validity, as well as the cause of the anticipated or unconscious anxiety. Nonverbal communication may be distorted to fit the perceiver's unconscious projection, provoking the undesired reaction against which the defense was originally constructed. The group therapist may also question the non-accepting members about why they cannot accept behavior or defenses which differ from their own. Contagion throughout the group of the hostile reaction of one member against the addict or the latter's behavior may also be explored. This affords the opportunity of determining whether the hostility is experienced by all or whether the contagion is a result of a need to conform to the attitude of the original hostile figure, or of other needs. It is thus possible to use even destructive acting-out behavior to further the progress of the therapeutic process.

Very often, the drug addict has a tendency to miss many sessions or to leave the group for varying periods of time and then return. There is also a possibility that the addict may have to be removed from the group for other reasons. Departure or removal of the addict may result in creating intense anxiety within the remaining group members. The departure of the addict may provoke feelings of guilt within the others because they have "disappointed" him or have been unable to help him. They may also feel, through their identification with the "lost" member, that their problem is insoluble and they, in turn, will be "forced out." The group therapist may use these reactions advantageously by exploring the identification with the addict, as well as the meaning of the hostility which had been experienced toward the patient who has left. The anxiety and guilt stimulated by the departure may also be reduced by the therapist's clarifying the extent of the addict's emotional problem and the other factors involved in his need to leave.

If the addict has an exceptionally low tolerance for anxiety, there is a special need for him to be seen in combined therapy. Individual sessions may also offer the therapist additional opportunity to help the patient work out and contain his anxiety at a tolerable level, decreasing his need to resort to drugs as a defense.

Alcoholism

Alcoholism is one of the most difficult problems to work with in an uncontrolled environment. While narcotics may act as a tranquillizer against the anxiety-provoking effect of emotional stimuli, alcohol very often tends to weaken prior inhibiting forces. When the alcoholic is placed in a psychotherapeutic group, the other members may accept the alcoholism as symptomatic, but it is often very difficult for them to tolerate a "drunk" within their circle. When inebriated, the alcoholic may try to act out with other patients outside as well as during the therapeutic session. He may try to force himself upon them, demanding that they provide gratification for his needs, *e.g.*, act as a watchdog to prevent him from drinking, provide alcohol or money to buy it, or "wet nurse" him when he is intoxicated. A great number of alcoholics who come into treatment also become members of Alcoholics Anonymous. One of the major threats experienced by the alcoholic is that of being rejected because he may be seen as a social deviate or asocial. It may be most advantageous for the alcoholic to maintain his membership in or join an Alcoholics Anonymous group even though he is in psychotherapy. Membership in the Alcoholics Anonymous promotes a feeling of belonging, as well as offering some controls which usually cannot be attained in other ways. Such controls may include taking care of the alcoholic when inebriated, staying with him and preventing him from drinking when he is experiencing intense anxiety. The aid available through other Alcoholics Anonymous members will diminish the patient's need to act out and to make unacceptable demands on the group members.

If inebriated during the group session, the alcoholic may behave in a destructive and uninhibited manner and show lack of self-control. He may unleash unprovoked and displaced hostility toward any number or all group members, inducing intense retaliatory feelings. This type of reaction may, in turn, be used by other members to reinforce their own resistances to therapy and/or stimulate overt and destructive acting out. This kind of behavior may lead the other group members to regard the alcoholic with contempt. The perception of alcoholism as symptomatic is often overshadowed by intense sympathy for his family and the alcoholic usually becomes the object of intense abuse and hostility[12-18].

The family of the addict, narcotic as well as alcoholic, is a very important factor in his recovery. It may be most advantageous and sometimes even a necessity that the therapist maintain liaison with the patient's spouse. He can maintain liaison with the parents if the patient is unmarried and living with them. As the therapist cannot possibly maintain a 24-hour vigilance with any patient, family members of the addicts may be encouraged to participate in the over-all recovery process. When possible, it may be most beneficial to have family members in treatment, preferably in a group with family members of other addicts. The group process offers the family an opportunity to understand common problems which are created by the addict and find more adequate means of coping with them.

The alcoholic is usually unable to tolerate the negative reactions to him and often leaves the group. It is all the more important that the alcoholic be seen in intermittent and when possible regularly scheduled individual sessions in addition to the group session. The group therapist may find it advantageous to have the individual session immediately following the group. This procedure provides an opportunity for alleviating intolerable anxiety which may have been provoked during the group session.

The group therapist must remember that he is responsible for the psychotherapeutic welfare of each member, as well as the group as an entity. It is important that he not allow the other group members to use the alcoholic as a scapegoat. Also, he must be aware of the possibility and not let the other group members be "sucked in" to gratify the masochistic needs of the alcoholic. He can explore what might be done with the spouse and family of the addict or alcoholic, as an adjuvant to therapy.

Sociopaths

Several types of psychopathology may be placed in the category of sociopaths: exhibitionists, voyeurs, homosexuals, and other sexual deviates[19-23]. Although these persons may be effectively treated in a group, it is important to consider the group constellation in the placement of these patients. The anxiety and acting out provoked in the group by the sociopath requires that the number of patients of this kind be limited within each group. The inclusion of one sociopath may have a positive effect on the psychotherapeutic process, but more than two may result in such negative effects as to destroy the group.

There are several advantages in placing a sociopath in a psychotherapeutic group. These advantages are related to the therapeutic process of the group, the other group members and to the sociopath himself. First, acceptance of these persons by the therapist implicitly means that the therapist regards the sociopath's drives, desires, and behavior as acceptable for discussion in the group. They are seen as the overt manifestations of the patients' problem. The behavior is seen as a symptomatic manifestation. The inclusion of the sociopath is discussed in relationship to characteristics and/or symptoms, not as a humorous tidbit. The other group members, although they may be fearful at first, will begin to understand that the deviate's behavior pattern is a symptom of his conflicts and problems and is best regarded as a symptom.

The acting out of the sociopath is not necessarily an indication that he is more severely disturbed than other group members, or that he is someone to be rejected. He has problems which are to be explored and analyzed just like everyone else's. Reaction to the sociopath in the group may provoke intense conflicts of the other members which previously have been repressed. As the other group members begin to express their previously unconscious conflicts, they may then begin to explore, analyze, and cope with their feelings about the sociopath. The ego-alien characteristic of the deviate's externalized symptoms may have a very positive effect in differentiating between the individual and his behavior. As one patient put it, "He really is a nice guy: I never thought that sexual deviates are such nice guys." Some members of the group may overtly express their intense fear of the deviate. This reaction usually manifests the individual's intense fear of what he experiences as deviate drives. One patient said, "I used to be very much afraid of having anything to do with anyone who showed any deviation from what I thought was normal sexual behavior." Another noted, "I guess it was because I must have had an unconscious fear that I might get involved with them and act out some of my own homosexual feelings."

The exploration and discussion of these ego-alien drives allow the group members the opportunity to become aware of and work out these infantile needs and drives. Thus, they are able to gain insight and work through their conflicts, resulting in greater freedom and mature sexual activity.

Limiting the number of sociopaths in a group to one or two is most important. The flooding of a group with a large number of persons who exhibit deviate and/or asocial behavior may create an atmosphere of condoning these behavior patterns and perhaps perpetuate and encourage acting out rather than working through of the underlying conflicts. Instead of working through their problems, the group members may preserve the group as a place for getting together and continually acting out over and over again. It is the therapist's responsibility to accept and utilize the acting out which occurs in a group for analytic purposes, but not to condone, encourage, or perpetuate the compulsive continuation of these patterns.

The social deviate in the group usually feels extremely threatened at the beginning of his group experience. The male deviate fears that the women will seduce him and rob him of his homosexual way of life. The other males in the group may experience the threat of being seduced by the homosexual. The female homosexual is much less likely to express concern about leaving her way of life. The deviate of either sex usually anticipates intense anxiety resulting from the admission of his behavior. He fears rejection for being a deviate and of being ostracized by the other group members.

The voyeur may try to induce other group members to exhibit themselves. At the same time, he may experience intense anxiety that he will be discovered. The exhibitionist may become panic-stricken by his compulsive drives to exhibit himself, which may result in rejection. Thus, the group therapist should be sensitive to the building-up of intense anxiety of the sociopath, as he struggles against the intense drive to act out. If the anxiety is not worked out, the deviate may become truly paralyzed in the group.

Psychosomatic Problems

There have been many different classifications of problems into the category of psychosomatic illnesses. We regard psychosomatic illnesses as organic ailments which have been initiated and/or exacerbated by emotional conflicts, like peptic ulcers, asthma, and migraine headaches[24-26].

Psychosomatic illnesses are most often treated without the benefit of any psychotherapy. More recently, the recognition of possible emotional factors in such illnesses has resulted in an increase in the referral of these problems for psychotherapeutic help. When considering the planning of such treatment the therapist must once more consider the advantages as well as the disadvantages of individual, group and combined treatment. Since the individual's inability to cope appropriately with anxiety is related to his organic malady, the group psychotherapist must scrutinize the effect of group reactions on the individual patient. As in all probems, the therapy should be directed toward the cause of the individual's condition, rather than his overt behavior. The therapist must determine the goal of treatment before deciding on the treatment plan. Is the treatment to be limited to symptom alleviation, working through the precipitating cause of the reaction or working through personality factors which make the individual susceptible to such reactions? The therapist must also keep in mind the anxiety tolerance of the patient and whether the group experience of the individual will produce an acute reaction or help him to gain insight into his problems and hence more effectively cope with them. The therapist should be cautious about creating unrealistic expectations in the patient. It may be propitious to inform the patient that psychotherapy will not cure his somatic difficulties, but may diminish the effects as the anxiety is reduced.

It has been found best to limit a heterogeneous group to one or two patients with psychosomatic problems. These patients have a tendency to fasten onto and restrict their discussions to organic problems. They often feel that they are different from the other people because their problem is organic rather than emotional. Having more than two people with psychosomatic problems in a heterogeneous group may result in subgrouping, and the accompanying resistance may block their own as well as the group's movement and progress. The advantages of a heterogeneous group for such problems, however, are many. Their advantages often more than compensate for the possible intensity of anxiety which these persons experience. In such a group, other members will offer an atmosphere in which the organic factors become secondary and the underlying emotional conflicts become the focus for exploration. The other members of the group in their interactions with this patient are able to become aware of the relationships between behavior and psychosomatic disorders.

It may be wise to consider inclusion of psychosomatic problems into a homogeneous group, because of the possible dangers of intense anxiety which may be mobilized in the group, resulting in severe acute attacks. A homogeneous setting has the advantage of helping to contain the anxiety at a tolerable level. Each person, being sensitive to his own organic disorder and attempting to prevent intensification of anxiety, tends not to explore or provoke this anxiety in others. The mobilization of anxiety in the homogeneous group is controlled by all members of the group and not left entirely up to the therapist. The members' very concentration on their organic problems may even be an asset in treatment. When the therapist feels that the group members are ready to delve more intensely into their emotional conflicts, he may easily question their need to restrict the discussion to somatic problems. This questioning alone tends to create anxiety which the members may then explore and relate to the accompanying somatic reaction and/or exacerbation.

Psychosomatic symptoms and problems must be coped with in group psychotherapy in very much the same way as they are in individual treatment. The somatic problem is a defense mechanism of the individual developed as one means of coping with anticipated overwhelming anxiety[27]. This defense mechanism must not be attacked by the therapist. Results of the anxiety which may be experienced when the defense mechanism has been removed must be evaluated by the therapist. Most frequently, the patient's feeling that his defenses will be destroyed will result in an attempted intensification of the defense. If the patient's needed defense is removed before he has another "crutch" to replace it or has attained sufficient ego strength, he may resort to acute psychotic reactions. The therapist will do well to work toward the increase of ego strength to enable the patient to cope with his emotional conflicts. In so doing, he will increasingly be able to relinquish his somatic problems as a defense[28].

Special Behavior Problems: Psychotherapeutic Group

The special qualities of the psychotherapeutic group provide the opportunity for the appearance of specific behavior patterns which are not displayed in individual psychotherapy. These behavior patterns may be manifestations of the individual and/or individual's character structure or of defenses which protect the individual's ego against an anticipated overwhelming threat. A description of some of these *behaviors* may aid the group therapist in knowing what to look for, as well as in understanding these patterns which are not observed in individual treatment.

Passive Dependency

The passive dependent type demonstrates helplessness, indecision and clinging to others[29]. In the group, the passive-dependent individual very often will select and/or be induced to form relationships with those persons who, in contrast, have a strong need to dominate. The passive-dependent will often be seen to acquiesce, becoming a "yes-man" or "lackey." Instead of reacting against and exploring the justification of demands placed upon him, this patient will seek gratification for his infantile needs by means of subservience. Very often, this behavior pattern will lead to a sado-masochistic relationship which may prove to be very destructive.

An example of this situation is Jack, a 36-year-old male, who was never able to experience any feeling of acceptance by his mother. Throughout his life, he continually sought someone who might be accepting and loving. In the group, Jack continually developed mother-child relationships indiscriminately, seeking to have his strong infantile needs gratified by going along with any and all demands placed upon him. If someone needed a scapegoat upon whom to vent aggression, Jack would assume this role. If someone needed adulation, Jack would flatter him. Outside the group sessions, Jack was the first to reach for the check when the group members went for coffee and he was always available for favors. His constant effort was an unsuccessful attempt to be taken under someone's wing, and by being a "good little boy," "mother" would respond by love and gratification of his strong oral dependency needs. Only after Jack was made aware of this behavior pattern, was he able to explore and analyze its development. He then learned that his behavior resulted only in perpetuating his already intense frustration, because his relationships were restricted to those who made demands upon him. Whenever he would seek gratification of his own needs, he would immediately be dropped. If such relationships are not picked up and made a focus by the therapist, the passive-dependent individual will experience himself in a continually exploited position. This exploitation will either reinforce and perpetuate his infantile drives and/or force him to leave the group because of the resulting anxiety-arousing frustration.

Exhibitionism

The group may offer the exhibitionist—and voyeur—an excellent opportunity for acting out his deviant behavior. Group members, like all persons, enjoy a bit of "spice" and tend to accept, and on occasions to encourage exhibitionistic behavior. Rudolph, a 28-year-old male overt homosexual, frequently related his sexual exploits to the group. He would describe finding girls' telephone numbers in phone booths and on public lavatory walls. He would then call and attempt to seduce these girls over the telephone. His stories would captivate the group's attention—the men identifying with his aggressive exploits, the women identifying with being sexually exploited. Although the group continued to wait for Rudolph's exploits to result in a successful relationship, he would relate that his "success" was restricted to having the woman he called give him a verbal lashing over the phone or, if he actually met them, slap or reject him some other way.

The group members' anxiety-provoking frustration finally resulted in a severe attack upon Rudolph. Here in the group, Rudolph through his exhibitionistic display had once again proven that he was able to control and frustrate people. The attack upon him by the group members was proof of his ability to control and manipulate people to serve his homosexual needs to be "attacked," "raped." It is important that the therapist be sensitive to and understand the meaning of this kind of pattern. If such behavior is allowed to continue unchecked, the group members may experience the therapist's acceptance as an indication of approval. They may feel that such behavior should be continued rather than being material for analysis.

Assistant Therapist

Very often, the therapist may find that he has "an assistant therapist" amongst the group members. This member will tend to take over the supposed functions of the therapist by asking leading questions of the other members, analyzing behavior and being always ready with an interpretation. Adoption of this "assistant therapist's" role may be a result of one or more of many factors. The patient may be the therapist's helper in an attempt to ingratiate himself and by so doing acquire the therapist's support in gratifying his own dependency needs. Or, in contrast, the patient may experience intense rivalry with the therapist and attempt to destroy him by displaying himself as a much more competent, helpful, and need-satisfying parent figure.

The therapist must be cautious of the possible destructive effect of the "assistant therapist's" role. It is advantageous for members of the group to assume leadership to develop ability to understand and help others. However, the therapist must be cautious and understand the underlying motivation for the group member or group members assuming this role. Very often, the therapist may experience this group member as very helpful and productive to the group and may allow himself to be induced to take a back seat in the activity of the group. If this occurs, the group members may experience the therapist as abdicating his authority to the "assistant therapist." This can result only in the destruction of the therapist's authority role and considerable loss in the therapeutic value of his contributions to the group interaction.

The therapist has the primary responsibility for the therapeutic progress of the group and its respective members. If the therapist relinquishes his authority role, thus his responsibility to the group members, his presence in the group has no constructive purpose. This situation is comparable to the lecture where the speaker informs the audience that he knows no more about the subject than any one in the audience. If the speaker is neither an expert nor someone who is able to increase the audience's knowledge, he has no business being on the podium. He should join the audience and obtain an authority on the subject to take his place. Similarly, the therapist cannot abrogate his responsibilities.

Silent Member

Silence on the part of a patient may be experienced in group as well as individual psychotherapy. In individual treatment, the therapist is able to explore and analyze the silence with a minimum threat to the patient. In the group situation, however, silence may be more symptomatic of the patient's emotions and feelings. More importantly, silence may be a defense mechanism against an anticipated overwhelming anxiety which is experienced as a destructive threat to his ineffective ego strength. However, the silence may be experienced by other group members exclusively as hostile negativism and/or rejection of them by the silent member. Most frequently, they will encourage the silent member to join them in anticipating a group interaction by means of direct invitation, cajoling, and sometimes direct threats.

If silence is merely the result of reluctance to adapt to the strangeness of the group situation, encouragement by other members usually results in its evaporation. However, if the silence is a defense mechanism against anticipated overwhelming anxiety, any attack by other group members may result in an intensification of the defense or a running-away by the patient in order to protect himself. If the patient's silence is a necessary defense, the therapist must permit its continuation until the ego strength of the patient is sufficient to give it up. Silence and variations of silence such as falling asleep during a group session, may be pointed out to the other group members as a necessary means of protection. If the other group members are unable to accept this patient's defense, their own anxieties may be material for analysis. The group therapist must remember that all patients who function as silent members cannot be classified in the same group. Some patients are silent as a defense against intense anxiety; others are silent because of a lack of contact with reality. There are, however, some members who remain silent and yet are quite involved within the emotional interaction of the group process. These persons, although silent, may make progressive strides through their identification with other members, as well as nonverbally working through their conflicts.

Silence by a group member does not necessarily mean complete withdrawal. The silent patient may benefit therapeutically by observing and identifying himself with other members of the group in their participation and interactions. As the threat to his own ego diminishes, he may participate more actively in the group. Periodic silences may be observed and related to specific activities and topics which tend to intensify the patient's anxiety. Once the group has been made aware of these anxiety-arousing situations, it may work toward overcoming the threat which the group member experiences. As it does so successfully, the silent member will increasingly be able to relinquish his formerly necessary defense. He may modify his participation in the group from nonverbal to verbal communication.

Provocateur

The provocateur, as the name implies, is the individual who provokes in the group session. The provocateur may be characterized as the "irritant," "stimulant," "Devil's advocate," and similar names.

As patients within a group are relatively tolerant to aggressive action from other members, it is often advantageous for the group constellation to include a provocateur. This group member's behavior may be constructive or destructive, depending upon the understanding of the therapist and how he utilizes the resulting interactions within the group. The provocateur often may assume an aggressive, probing, and questioning attitude within the group. This tends to stimulate the other persons, both in examining their own feelings and thinking and reacting to outside disturbing elements. The provocateur's actions within the group may often allow the therapist to reserve his own probing for analysis and interpretations rather than having to be overactive within the group situation. There are innumerable variations in how the provocateur may "operate" within the group.

A negative and destructive example is Stanley, who, through his efforts, was successful in eliminating at least three new members from the group. Stanley was a 40-year-old hostile, dependent person who could not experience satisfaction for his intense dependency needs. He constantly sought the full attention of the therapist and said that he felt rejected when the therapist became involved in any situation in which he was not a focal point. When any new member entered the group, Stanley would immediately begin to question the reason for the new member's entrance and would discourage his continuing in the group by berating the therapist's competence and the effectiveness of group psychotherapy. His continued barrage would create such anxiety that the new member would flee. When other members attempted to stop this behavior, Stanley would counteract their efforts with a hostile barrage, saying, "I am only expressing my feelings and that's the reason we are here. Are you rejecting me too? You are only giving lip service to the idea that we are supposed to express our feelings and thoughts freely. Actually, you want to shut me up, the same as my mother always did. She would encourage me to tell her how I felt about things and then would reject me because my thinking did not go along completely and totally with hers." The therapist's lack of understanding of what Stanley was doing initially stopped him as well as the group members from being able to cope adequately with this situation. The therapist, not wanting to induce a feeling of rejection in Stanley, tended to condone rather than analyze his behavior.

After losing several patients as a result of Stanley's negative provocation, the therapist began to explore his own reactions as well as Stanley's. He began to realize that Stanley had induced him into a counter-transference relationship where he anticipated intense guilt if there were any negative responses to Stanley's actions. Actually, his laissez-faire behavior had resulted in condoning and reinforcing Stanley's feelings that any negative response meant rejection. The next time Stanley began to provoke in an effort to eliminate competitive rivals for attention, the therapist began to explore both Stanley's need to annihilate rivals as well as the other patients' reactions to his provocative behavior. The exploration brought out Stanley's early experience of being the center of parental attention until the birth of a sibling, when he was 5 years old. With the arrival of the sibling, the attention that was previously all his began to be divided between himself and the sibling. This occurrence had resulted in his experiencing feelings of intense rejection and any attempt to regain his lost position would result in punitive action by the parents. Following the analysis of this destructive behavior pattern, Stanley continued to be provocative, but the provocation was in the direction of stimulating the other members to explore and probe for underlying meaning and associations to their own reactions.

References

1. ABRAMS, A. *et al.*, Group therapy with narcotic addicts, method and evaluation. *Group Psychotherapy* 11:244, 1958.
2. BAILEY, W. C., Individual counselling and group psychotherapy with paroled drug addicts: a pilot field experiment. *Research Studies of the College of Washington* 24:141, 1956.
3. BRUNNER-ORNE, M., The utilization of group psychotherapy in enforced treatment programs of alcoholics and addicts. *Internat. J. Group Psychotherapy* 6:272, 1956.
4. FORT, J. P., The psychodynamics of drug addiction and group psychotherapy. *Internat. J. Group Psychotherapy* 5:150, 1955.
5. HASKELL, M., The drug addict, role playing and group psychotherapy, the need for a new approach. *Group Psychotherapy* 11:197, 1958.
6. McLAIN, J., An experiment in group psychotherapy with the narcotic addict. *Am. J. Psychotherapy* 5:24, 1951.
7. OSBERG, J. W., and BERLINER, A. K., The developmental stages in group psychotherapy with hospitalized narcotic addicts. *Internat. J. Group Psychotherapy* 6:436, 1956.
8. ROSENTHAL, V., and SHIMBERG, E., A program of group therapy with incarcerated narcotic addicts. *J. Criminal Law, Criminol. Police Sci.* 49:140, 1958.
9. THORPE, J. J., and SMITH, B., Phases in group development in the treatment of drug addicts. *Internat. J. Group Psychotherapy* 3:66, 1953.
10. THORPE, J. J., "Addicts," in SLAVSON, S. R., *The Fields of Group Psychotherapy*. New York, International Universities Press, 1956, pp. 59–75.

11. YABLONSKY, L., Group psychotherapy and psychodrama for drug addicts. *Nat. Probation & Parole J.* 5:63, 1953.

12. BRUNNER-ORNE, M., and ORNE, M. T., Directive group therapy in the treatment of alcoholics: techniques and rationale. *Internat. J. Group Psychotherapy* 4:293, 1953.

13. GREENBAUM, H., Group therapy with alcoholics in conjunction with antabuse treatment. *Internat. J. Group Psychotherapy* 4:30, 1953.

14. STEWART, D. A., Empathy in the group therapy of alcoholics. *Quart. J. Study of Alcohol* 15:288, 1954.

15. FEIBER, C., The archaic personality structure of alcoholics and its implications for group therapy. *Internat. J. Group Psychotherapy* 9:1, 1960.

16. LINDT, H., The "rescue fantasy" in group treatment of alcoholics. *Internat. J. Group Psychotherapy* 9:43, 1959.

17. PRESTON, F., Combined individual, joint and group therapy in the treatment of alcoholism. *Ment. Hyg.* 44:522, 1960.

18. EWING, J. A., LONG, V., and WENZEL, G. G., Concurrent group psychotherapy of alcoholic patients and their wives. *Internat. J. Group Psychotherapy* 11:329, 1961.

19. CORSINI, R. J., Group psychotherapy with a hostile group. *Group Psychotherapy* 6:168, 1954.

20. TEIRICH, H. R., Group psychotherapy in sexual problems. *Internat. J. Sexology* 7:199, 1954.

21. STERN, E., Group psychoanalysis with individuals manifesting sexual deviate patterns. *Acta Psychotherapeutica Psychosomatica et Orthopaedagogica* 7: Suppl. 365, 1959.

22. DURKIN, H., GLATZER, H., KADIS, A. L., WOLF, A., and HULSE, W., Acting out in group psychotherapy: a panel discussion. *Am. J. Psychotherapy* 11:57, 1958.

23. BRY, T., Acting out in group psychotherapy. *Internat. J. Group Psychotherapy* 3:42, 1953.

24. STONE, A., and LEVINE, L., Group therapy in sexual maladjustment. *Am. J. Psychiat.* 107:195, 1950.

25. KLEIN, H. S., Psychogenic factors in dermatitis and their treatment by group therapy. *Psychoanalyt. Rev.* 39:376, 1952.

26. STEIN, A., Group psychotherapy in patients with peptic ulcer. *Arch. Neurol. Psychiat.* 73:580, 1952.

27. HOLT, H., and WINICK, C., Group psychotherapy with obese women. *Arch. Gen. Psychiat.* 5:156, 1961.

28. IGERSHEIMER, W. W., Analytically oriented group psychotherapy for patients with psychosomatic illness. The selection of patients and the forming of groups. *Internat. J. Group Psychotherapy* 9:71, 1959.

29. ABRAHAMS, J., and VARON, E., Maternal dependency and schizophrenia: mothers and daughters in a therapeutic group. New York, International Universities Press, 1953.

termination of treatment 11

THE MAJORITY of psychotherapists increasingly think in terms of recovery rather than in terms of cure. A logical question therefore has to do with what constitutes recovery. How can we assess the patient's readiness to terminate treatment?

It is emphasized that there are no simple barometers of recovery, and those that exist must be used with caution. An individual patient's recovery can be assessed only in the light of his previous degree of disturbance and his potential for further improvement. One patient at the termination of his group therapeutic experience may be less able to cope with certain problems than another patient may be before he begins a similar experience. There are some key qustions which may be asked about any patient whose termination is being considered: How much nearer is the patient to the resolution of his core conflict and of other significant conflicts? How much better can he function than he could before? In what areas has he overcome, or greatly diminished, his malfunctioning? Has he reached a point of diminishing return in treatment? No one yardstick for termination can be used on a group in its entirety, because each individual member can only be assessed against the benchmark of his pretherapy functioning, personality, and reality situation[1].

Even in the most homogeneously organized groups, differences in character structure, psychopathology, and individual resources call for differentiated evaluation of each patient's readiness to terminate. The therapist will hopefully be able to help each member accept and

149

realize not only his own uniqueness but the uniqueness of all his peers in the group. When this becomes apparent to them, the group members will not expect the therapist to treat them all in the same way. They will also perceive and recognize the value of individual differences, and realize that understanding is often achieved through differences, as well as through identification[2]. As the patient gradually consolidates insights of this kind, he will know that his readiness to terminate will be gauged not by a common yardstick but by his own personal yardstick, which his uniqueness demands.

The methods of terminating group-therapy patients are different from those used in individual therapy[3]. A patient in individual therapy may be terminated abruptly or after a "weaning period" in which sessions are gradually reduced, perhaps from several weekly sessions to monthly sessions, until therapy is discontinued altogether. But in group settings it is not feasible to permit patients to come and go on an irregular basis. Such a procedure would disrupt the integrity and therapeutic movement of the group, and the loss of content and continuity of many sessions would put group members at a great disadvantage. Other techniques must therefore be employed to permit the patient to work through any flare-up of old symptoms, as well as remnants of primary separation anxiety, before terminating treatment entirely. He can accomplish this purpose either in the group setting or in individual sessions after terminating with the group.

The tapering-off period for patients in group therapy may involve a few or many individual sessions. Some therapists rely heavily on a whole battery of personality tests to help them decide on patients' readiness for termination. Such tests include the Rorschach, figure drawing, T.A.T., mosaic, and sentence-completion[4]. But it must be stressed that the findings of such tests can be considered valid only if the same tests are given before treatment is begun and when termination is considered. There is a practical application of the "personal" yardstick. There are as yet not enough carefully correlated data on "before-and-after" tests to be sure of what they reveal in the way of clinical improvement. Some investigators in the psychometric field believe that a patient's total gains from treatment cannot be revealed by tests made immediately after termination because he requires time to integrate them. Other means of gauging recovery, as shown by long-term gains, may emerge from current research on this subject.

Patients in group therapy usually indicate their readiness to terminate, and this can be a healthy sign in itself. How does the therapist respond? In all cases he may well ask, "Why do you think you are ready to leave?" The patient tries to assess himself and his current level of functioning, and group members offer evaluations of their own. The resulting interaction yields valuable clues to the extent of the patient's recovery and to the amount of pathology that still remains. It is common practice for the therapist to ask the patient to stay with the group for a while, and sometimes to schedule individual sessions with him, to make sure that his wish to leave does not represent acting out of any transference resistance. The patient's agreement to these measures augurs well for his readiness to be on his own. But if he insists that he must leave right away or next week, without any visible reason for doing so, an acting-out transference resistance may be suspected.

Some examples of healthy termination, often called "graduation" by the group, will convey some of the flavor of the situation.

Janet entered treatment in her early thirties after her husband had divorced her because of her inadequacy as a wife and as a mother to their child, and because her quarrelsomeness made any friendships or solid family relationships impossible. During her first two years in the group, she found the going rough. Her anger and hostility were constantly directed against other members, and they in turn rejected her completely. "I don't see how your husband put up with you as long as he did." . . . "You're simply not willing to accept your role as a woman." . . . "You'd fight with the Angel Gabriel himself," were typical comments. Outside the group, she acted out sexually. Flamboyantly dressed and overly made-up, she ceaselessly sought a strong cave-man type of ideal mate, and inevitably discarded or was discarded by one man after another.

In her third year of group treatment, when she had come to understand her core problem much better, her anger and hostility began to diminish. At this time, she met a university professor who was also divorced and had one child. For the first time, she recognized and appreciated sensitivity and kindness in a man. "He can't give me all I once wanted—a handsome house, jewelry, furs, and servants," she said, "but I had them in my first marriage and couldn't have been unhappier. Now I think I'm grown up enough to want what he *can* give me—stability, kindness, thoughtfulness, and love. I guess my phony values are getting straightened out at last." She married this man with whom she saw the opportunity of developing a fuller-shared emotional life. At the group's request, she agreed to remain for another ten weeks after her marriage. After eight weeks, the group "let her off the hook" by saying "It's really unfair to keep you any longer, although you've been of endless help to us and we will all miss you."

Jack had spent four years in treatment (one alternate and two group sessions weekly) when he announced one day that he was ready to leave. "When I started therapy," he said, "I felt I'd never be able to write my Ph.D. thesis. My marriage seemed washed up, and I didn't think I'd ever give up drinking. Now my thesis has been accepted and my job prospects are good. I've got a sound marriage and we hope to have another child sometime. I'm sure I can support the family without my wife's shouldering most of the load as she had to do in the past. I haven't been in any brawls due to drinking for over two years, though if my thesis had been turned down I might have been sorely tempted to go on a one-night binge. I'll miss you all, especially Estelle. She's been a real friend and I hope our friendship will continue. She certainly helped me a lot; all of you have for that matter. If I get into a funk I can always call on you (nodding to the therapist). I think I've come a long way, and now I'm ready to stand on my own feet. I probably haven't done you much good, but I hope I've helped a little."

The other members discussed Jack's self-evaluation and, on the whole, agreed with it. The consensus was: "Stick around a while. Next month when the therapist is on vacation, we'll need you at our alternate meetings, and you may be glad to have us around." Jack agreed to this plan, terminating his treatment only after the therapist returned.

At other times, the group may resent any member's leaving. His contemplated action may evoke all the competitiveness of the others. "He is ready to fly, but I'm so dependent on you, Dr. B., and the group family that I must stay," is a typical comment. The departing member may be attacked, rejected, or exposed to frustration. His ability to take such hostile tactics in stride generally speaks well for his readiness to terminate. His attitude toward the others may express feelings like this: "I understand why you're mad at me and I'm sorry about it. I don't mind staying a little longer, maybe a month or two, but I still feel I'm ready to leave."

A practice in some psychotherapy groups is the "going around" technique[5]. When a patient is about to leave, other members usually ask him to give his impressions of them. If this request doesn't come spontaneously from the group members, the therapist may wish to initiate it. Both patients and therapist may learn a great deal from such impromptu assessments of the members' progress. An example will help to illustrate the kind of material brought up in the "going around" technique before termination.

Jane was a patient who had been in the group for three years. When she spoke of leaving the group, the other patients actively disagreed with her. She agreed to stay on. Several months later, she announced, "I've decided to leave next week. I think it is a good time for me to stop. My whole family is leaving for a vacation. I really think I'm ready to leave." To this comment, two group members, one male and one female, stated how much they would miss her and how much she added "spark to the group." Jane responded, "I think you are right. I feel my own strength right now, and at the same time I'm feeling slightly frustrated at the broken record of the group and my inability to really latch on to your problems today. At any rate I have the feeling that I have given something to you, and also that I have really received a great deal from each one of you."

At this point the therapist asked Jane to "go around" and tell the other group members how she felt about them. Jane said to Manfred, "You said once that you were sorry that you hadn't given more to me. I felt it was almost something in myself that I was seeing in you—something that I had been and at times still am—angry. You reminded me of my mother, and being able to see this and experience you as my mother made me understand what it really was that bothered me in my mother. This was very helpful, and I find myself becoming more and more tolerant of your 'weaknesses' since I realize it's not only you, it's not only my mother, I too do the same things. There is nothing tangible that you gave me, never verbal advice, but a feeling of responding back and forth so that I could actually feel my feelings of anger and frustration and sometimes know how to handle them. I really like you, Manfred."

Jane then turned to Rose, a married woman with two children who was separated from her husband. "I feel, Rose, you are my friend, and I feel very warm and loving toward you. You have said in the past that you don't understand my 'problem' but this doesn't matter now. You don't have to understand my problem as long as you are with me and there is a mutual feeling of closeness between us. At first I felt that I didn't know in what way you had helped me, but I have just realized at this moment that you were the biggest help of all. By seeing you as the good mother who could relish sex, I feel and truly believe that to be a woman can be freeing. I think what I am trying to say is that without really realizing it the group gave me themselves. I feel that I will continue to see Rose sometimes in the future."

At this point Rose replied, "You will never know how helpful you have been to me—especially your probing and your anger." Then Jane turned to Will and said, "I like you very much. I could separate the times I felt that you were my brother, and I know that I will not again react to you or my brother as I have in the past. I feel very comfortable with you, respect you and would have liked to have you as a friend. I'm very sorry that you are going through such difficult times now, and somehow disappointed that are not able at the moment to pull yourself out of it. When I first started to talk about my feelings in relation to the group I interrupted Pen. You did not understand why I felt that you really weren't tackling your problem, and I know you were extremely angry with me. I remember once saying that that was my problem. Michael agreed with me that it wasn't just my problem, and I was glad to see that Pen's anger wasn't reaching me. I am having a hard time understanding what you have given me."

She paused, and continued, "You made me feel that I could be a little more tolerant of you. In other words, by your being as you are I was able to express my irritations and frustrations with you. Your irritating qualities were the thing that I latched on to most of the time, and I couldn't even see that you had a problem of feeling like a woman as I had had. I couldn't stop wondering why you didn't take my advice and give up seeing your boy friend, why you kept on the same treadmill. But now I begin to realize that's your problem and that neither you nor anybody else can do what I say or advise, but that each one of us has to work it out on his own. I was relating it to myself when I felt that I had been on a treadmill with my husband, and why I just didn't do what I knew I should do. By now I know it isn't that simple, and I get the feeling that I can be much more tolerant of Pen when I'm aware of it. Then I am able to push aside your side-tracking issues.

I feel that you're just as married as the rest of us and that you, as all of us, don't make the most of your freedom and your youth."

Pen tried to return a compliment to Jane, saying that she had received something valuable from her. Jane returned to Pen by saying, "Just now I realize more strongly than ever before that you have a problem of feeling like a woman." To this again Pen responded right away with, "You may be thinking of me as your sister and may be envying the freedom of my environment." Jane smiled at that and showed no irritation whatsoever.

Jane next turned to Tony and said, "I don't think there is too much warmth between us. I really don't know the reason for it, but I think it's because you haven't been with us too long. I don't yet know your problems. I don't feel too related to you, although I like you very much. I guess what I'm saying is that you didn't give yourself to me. You, Kurt, have been in the group such a short time that I feel we haven't mutually given much to each other. You, Michael, gave me something more tangible in a way than anyone else in the group. You are the only male who has even seen me as a woman, and this has been an extraordinary experience for me, although I don't feel I must go to bed with you to prove anything. You once said that you thought of me as being very tender, to which I replied, 'I was tender with my children, but it was much more difficult with adults.' Rose disagreed with me and said that she felt my tenderness. At that time I told her that it was hard to express it, but it is much easier now. And now I must tell you about my experience on the subway this morning. A young fellow looked at me, and I returned the look. I felt very attracted and womanly without feeling menaced for the first time in my life."

One member remarked, "You haven't said anything about us yet," to which Jane replied with a soft smile, "There isn't much to say. I just love you." At this point Will remarked that Jane's going around was the best "aloha" by a departing member. Michael added, "If anyone had doubts or questions whether Jane is ready to leave the group, we have no questions anymore. I didn't feel the same way about the two other members who left before." Everyone concurred, and it was time for the session to end.

There is one type of termination that is periodically initiated by the patients themselves[6]. This may be called the "seasonal" termination. It reflects the individual's life pattern extending back to school days when he was promoted to the next higher grade at the end of the term. Remaining in the same class—being "left back"—was associated with feelings of failure. Thus, at the end of any given year, a group member may suddenly say, "I've been here three years; how much longer will it take? I can't stay in treatment to the end of my days. I want to live instead of talking about it."

Or, he may say, "I've made a lot of progress and it's been all right, but I can finish now." The others pick up this refrain and in no time at all with but one or two exceptions the members of the group want to terminate treatment. All the skill of the group therapist is needed to analyze this resistance of the total group and of each individual member, without being affected by his own anxiety at the possibility of the group's suddenly vanishing before his eyes.

Another seasonal and contagious termination situation frequently occurs right after the therapist's vacation. The group is most often angry and resentful of being "dropped" for any length of time. "You took off and didn't worry about us," is the feeling they express, "and now we can leave you too."

During the first session after a therapist returned from a summer vacation, seven patients of a group of eight told him, with great logic and persuasiveness, that they had done so well in his absence they didn't need any more therapy. The remaining patient remarked, "I guess I'm the only one who isn't ready to leave. I'll have to go into another group, or another group will have to be started with me in it."

In the discussion that followed, the group members almost sheepishly discovered their need and desire to punish the therapist for what they considered his too-long vacation. Only one patient actually left at this time, and it turned out that he was the only one ready to go. The others had merely acted out a group resistance—the seasonal and contagious termination phenomenon[7].

In closed groups, the climate is affected by the time limit. A note of urgency is sounded in the frequently heard query, "Will we be ready to leave at the time we agreed on?" For some patients, the anxiety stemming from the termination date can be an added motivation toward health. But for others, it can hinder movement within themselves as well as in their relations within the group. These patients need assurance that it is not a question of "do or die." If they are not ready to terminate when this particular group is dissolved, they will have a chance to join another group, or find other therapeutic help that will meet their needs. Without this assurance, they may be so torn by doubts about their ability to "make it" that they will act out and leave prematurely. This is particularly likely to happen in the last stages of closed groups.

In open groups, it is understood that each member works at his own pace and is the ultimate judge of whether he is ready to leave. In such groups, separation anxiety over termination is not so acute. The patient in an open group is frequently confronted by the symbolic re-enactment of the universal problems and themes of life, death, and replacement. In this ever-recurring situation, he experiences and is compelled to come to terms with the unpalatable theme that runs through the lives of all: no one is indispensable. Termination is, of course, another expression of this inevitability. Acceptance of it and of its ramifications is yet another sign of maturity and of maturation[8].

These universal problems and themes that run through the life of an open group are bound to engender anxiety and tension. Again and again, patients must face conflicts arising when old members leave and new ones enter. The conflicts must be faced not only in relationship to their own lives but also via the lives of all other members.

For example, when Herb mentioned his decision to leave the group, Rose, who had established a strong father transference to him, became very anxious and begged him not to go. "I really need you to work out my relationship with my father," she said. "There's nobody else here to take his place. Father died before I was old enough to relate to him and tell him how much he meant to me."

A new member then said to Rose, "Nobody close to me has died, but I can see how important Herb is to you. The very thought that father could die, or that any member of my family might leave the city or even the block (they all lived in the same neighborhood) makes my pulse race. I want them all to stay together. . . . No, I mean I want *us* all to stay together."

The open group knows that if one member leaves, another is likely to replace him. And just as each patient is afraid of change, so the group itself fears anything new. "Who will come? What will happen?" The insecurity of those who dread the unknown (and who does not?) is sharpened by a dual anxiety—anxiety about the person who has gone and about the stranger coming into their lives.

Ellen said to the therapist, "It's all right when a member leaves the group; I like that. It gives me the feeling that someday I'll be able to say, 'The hell with you, I can fly on my own.' It gives me hope for myself. But when I think of the new member who'll take his place, I get angry with you. One is all to easily replaced in this life. When my mother died, father found another woman right away. If I die, I'm sure my husband will find another wife. I'm afraid he won't even wait a year."

Emphasis has been placed on methods for dealing with the group member who expresses the wish to terminate treatment. Unfortunately, in group as well as in individual therapy, the patient cannot always be counted on to bring up this subject. He may have become so firmly entrenched in his group sessions that he uses them as a substitute for a satisfactory life of his own outside. This is a particular hazard in groups very permissive to bizarre behavior, where the members do not insist that such behavior be analyzed and worked through. The patient may then become morbidly dependent on this environment for the habitual acting out of his disorder. In such instances, the therapist must analyze the patient's dependency on the group and help him to work through his core problem, thus freeing him for a satisfactory life outside.

The terminated patient who has not really resolved his transferences to the therapist and the group will try to hold on to its members on a private basis. A woman who voluntarily left her group telephoned a friend after each session. "What happened tonight? Who's taking my place? Let's have lunch and you can tell me all about it. I miss you all. Why don't you hold an alternate meeting here at my place?" This type of behavior is really acting out of a transference resistance and should be analyzed as such by the therapist and the patients who are still in the group. What unconscious needs of these patients are being met by this kind of relationship can be clarified and worked through.

Hindrances to Appraisal of Termination

The therapist's personality may on occasion interfere with his objective appraisal of the patient's readiness to terminate[9]. How aspiring is the therapist? How much of a perfectionist is he—not only for his patients but for himself? Just as an ambitious parent may bask in the reflected glory of his children, so a therapist may tend to drive his patients to ever greater analytic achievements in order to prove his superiority.

Positive and negative counter-transferences, as well as personal values and preferences, may enter into the therapist's evaluation of a patient's progress and readiness to terminate[10]. Sometimes he even accepts a patient without fee, in the unconscious hope that the patient may develop potentials and become the kind of person whose accomplishments will put "a feather in his cap." In such an instance, the therapist may unwittingly prolong the treatment, hoping against hope that the patient will achieve these "goals." But when he realizes that this is highly unlikely, the therapist's positive counter-transference may be replaced by a negative one. He may then convince himself that the patient has recovered and is ready to leave.

Before saying to a patient, "I think you should be on your own for a while," the therapist should examine his own motivations very closely. He should continuously question whether counter-transference feelings of anger or disappointment, thwarted wishful thinking about the therapeutic results, or similar factors, may underlie such a recommendation.

In general, the therapist should guard against a tendency to build castles in the air for patients. Since there is, of course, a limit to what a person can actually achieve, his recovery must be assessed in terms that are realistic for him and his particular life situation. Obviously, the recovery goal for an in-and-out institutionalized schizophrenic of 40 is different from that of a 25-year-old university instructor subject to severe attacks of anxiety.

Another hindrance to objective appraisal may be the patient's own expectations or those of his family. Often a patient enters therapy with a fantasy of being made over completely, to match his ideal self. Or, his family may demand that he become a pillar of society, the kind of person who will bring them status in the community. It is easy to see that his family's concept of recovery, the patient's concept, and the therapist's may sometimes be poles apart.

Take, for example, the case of a homosexual in his early forties who, before treatment, was unable to work or form any human relationships other than fleeting ones (as in subway toilets), and was completely dependent on his family for support. With the help of psychotherapy, he was in time able to obtain an academic degree, hold a very important and well-paid job. For the first time, he was able to establish a close relationship with another person, who now shares his life.

This patient was satisfied with his recovery; he became a well-functioning individual capable of achieving his goals. The therapist was only partially satisfied, having hoped that treatment would continue until the core problem of homosexuality was resolved. In the eyes of his family and the community, this patient had not recovered. He was still a homosexual, and they do not tolerate homosexuality.

Gauges of Recovery

How can we assess a patient's recovery as objectively as possible? It has been shown that the therapist's counter-transference feelings and the patient's transference feelings have to be taken into account, or distortions will be inevitable. It must be constantly kept in mind that each patient will be assessed only in relation to his former and potential self, and his peers. It is of course also true that the patient is carefully assessed throughout the whole course of therapy, not merely as he nears recovery. From his first day in treatment, the therapist notes evidences of worsening or betterment in certain areas of the patient's illness.

In the termination phase of treatment, the patient's goals may require adjustment, modification, and adaptation. He may also be reluctant or as yet unable to express positive affect, feelings of warmth, tenderness, and love. Thus when nearing the termination of treatment, the therapist must continuously evelute intrapsychic and intrapersonal situations.

The therapist may ask whether the patient takes his current life situation in stride and derives satisfaction from everyday activities, in contrast to living in the past or projecting himself into an unrealistic too-rosy future. Can he tolerate the inevitable frustrations of his social and home life and his job, without being thrown off or "stopped dead in his tracks?" The better he is able to cope with day-to-day frustrations, the better is his over-all adjustment.

The therapist may find the following rule-of-thumb helpful: recovery is directly related to the patient's capacity to work and to plan, to cooperate and to play, to love and be loved, and to use the tools of psychotherapy on his own to resolve problems affecting his mental health and well-being.

Another objective gauge of a patient's recovery includes increased freedom from free-floating anxiety, and from compulsion and rigidity. It also includes an increase in flexibility. When necessary, he can alter his levels of aspiration. He can change his attitude toward his mate, his children, his parents and other authority prototypes, and toward minorities. He simultaneously manifests growing independence and increased receptivity to healthier interdependent relationships.

One main criterion of recovery is the patient's improved interpersonal relations, both in and out of the group. He is wholesomely closer to family, friends, and colleagues. He is more positively involved with people, more rational, more flexible, and more discriminating in all his activities. When more free to explore himself and his environment, to disagree with what he hears, he achieves a fuller awareness of himself and of his personal world.

The patient approaching recovery will be less compelled to accept prevailing values in his environment without questioning their validity. Instead, he will be more eager and more able to seek his own values, and foster healthy growth. If his treatment has been successful, it has helped him achieve a sense of personal identity and an emotional "immunity level" that will protect him against infection by unhealthy and dehumanizing influences around him[11].

Coordinated meetings provide an additional means of gauging a patient's readiness to leave therapy[12]. In the two group settings, he can test his ability to function both with and without the help of expert authority[13]. If he behaves in the same realistic way in both instances, if his relationship with the authority and his peers is adequate, if he has been able to overcome a tendency to be too submissive or too bossy, he may be considered well on the road to recovery[14, 15]. As one group member told another, "I guess you are ready to leave. You can talk up when the therapist is here, and you don't push us around in alternate meetings. You aren't afraid of him and you aren't afraid of us either."

The patient ready to terminate is able to strike a balance between preoccupation with his own thoughts and behavior and consideration of the needs of others[16]. He feels increasingly free to express warm and tender feelings. He may have developed a loving relationship with his mate or with other family members, or his previous relationships with them may have deepened and become more satisfying. As calm replaces anxiety, his nightmares are replaced by dreams of more freely expressed wishes. Their latent content is less symbolically disguised and he shows less resistance to remembering and associating to them.

Psychotherapy cannot guarantee that any patient after termination will not be confronted with experiences beyond his frustration tolerance[17]. When such a patient hits a temporary rough spot, he is indeed fortunate if he can fall back on a former group member with whom he spent a significant part of his life and who then knew him as well as anyone else in the world.

Thus, the therapist should guard against interpreting all such friendships as merely transference relationships and thus contributing to their dissolution. One aim of therapy is to free the patient from dependency on the therapist. Therefore, seeking help from a former group member can be a sign of maturity. An ideally healthy peer relationship that may develop after successful termination of treatment is one of the distinct gains of group therapy.

References

1. KADIS, A. L., and WINICK, C., The role of the deviant in the psychotherapy group. *Internat. J. Social Psychiatry* 6:277, 1960.
2. WOLF, A., The Advanced and Terminal Phases in Group Psychotherapy. New York: *Proceedings, 2nd Annual Institute, American Group Psychotherapy Association,* Jan. 22–23, 1958.
3. BROSS, R. B., Termination of analytically oriented psychotherapy in groups. *Internat. J. Group Psychotherapy* 3:325, 1959.
4. ABT, L., and BELLAK, L., *Projective Psychology.* New York, Knopf, 1954.
5. WOLF, A., Psychoanalysis in groups. *Am. J. Psychotherapy* 3:525, 1959; 4:16, 1950.
6. LEOPOLD, H. S., The problem of working through in group psychotherapy. *Internat. J. Group Psychotherapy* 3:287, 1959.
7. SPOTNITZ, H., A psychoanalytic view of resistance in groups. *Internat. J. Group Psychotherapy* 1:3, 1952.
8. GROTJAHN, M., The process of maturation in group psychotherapy and in the group therapist. *Psychiatry* 13:63, 1950.
9. HADDEN, S. B., Countertransference in the group psychotherapist. *Internat. J. Group Psychotherapy* 4:417, 1953.
10. WOLF, A., and SCHWARTZ, E. K., Psychoanalysis in groups: the role of values. *Am. J. Psychoanalysis* 19:37, 1959.

11. WEISS, F. A., Discussion on social roots of the dream. *Am. J. Psychoanalysis* 20:180, 1960.
12. KADIS, A. L., The role of co-ordinated group meetings in group psychotherapy. *Acta Psychotherapeutica Psychosomatica Orthopaedagogica* 7:Suppl., 174, 1959.
13. KADIS, A. L., The alternate meeting in group psychotherapy. *Am. J. Psychotherapy* 10:275, 1956.
14. KADIS, A. L., "Alternate Meetings," in *Topical Problems of Psychotherapy*, Vol. 2. Karger, Basel, New York, 1960, p. 164.
15. WOLF, A., and SCHWARTZ, E. K., Psychoanalysis in groups: clinical and theoretical implications of the alternate meeting. *Acta Psychotherapeutica Psychosomatica et Orthopaedagogica* 7:Suppl., 404, 1959.
16. SPOTNITZ, H., *The Couch and the Circle*. New York, Knopf, 1961.
17. KITCHEN, R., On leaving group therapy. *Psychol. Newsletter,* New York Univ. 9:36, 1957.

training and professional 12
activities of group
psychotherapists

A FAIRLY clear picture of the American group psychotherapist today emerges from a questionnaire study of members of the American Group Psychotherapy Association[1]. The questionnaire was sent in 1960 to the entire membership of the association, of whom 64 per cent responded. This relatively high rate of response makes it very probable that the results of the study provide an accurate picture of the group psychotherapist in the United States.

It is interesting to see the geographic distribution of group psychotherapists. Almost a third (31 per cent) of the respondents are located in and around New York City. By region, 63 per cent are in the East, almost a fifth (17 per cent) in the West, 10 per cent in the Southern and 10 per cent in the Central part of the country. Group psychotherapists practice in communities of all sizes. Almost half (46 per cent) are in cities of over a million population, 16 per cent are in communities of a half million to a million, 14 per cent in communities of 100,000–499,999, and 24 per cent in smaller communities.

Professional Disciplines

A number of different professional disciplines are represented in the ranks of group psychotherapists. The M.D. is the highest academic degree reported by most, 43 per cent. Both M.D. and Ph.D. have been achieved by 1 per cent, the Ph.D. by 25 per cent, and the Ed.D. by 2 per cent. The M.S.S. or M.S.W. is held by 16 per cent, other Master's degrees by 10 per cent, a Divinity degree by 1 per cent and a Bachelor's degree by 1 per cent. The general clinical training of the respondents was obtained in a variety of settings: 22 per cent in a university, 15 per cent in a psychoanalytic training institute, 14 per cent in a Veterans' Administration hospital, 13 per cent in a general hospital's psychiatry department, 12 per cent in a state hospital, 8 per cent in a school of social work, 5 per cent in a medical school, and 4 per cent in a mental hospital which did not fall into these categories.

Nature and Length of Practice

The median group psychotherapist is involved in both private practice and institutional work, with 45 per cent giving private practice as their major activity, 37 per cent reporting their institutional affiliation as central, and 18 per cent reporting other activities (*e.g.*, teaching) as most salient.

The median group psychotherapist has been engaged in the practice of individual psychoanalysis or psychotherapy for 12.5 years. Almost three-fourths of group therapists (73 per cent) report that the practice of individual psychoanalysis or psychotherapy occupies at least over half of their practice; 52 per cent say it takes over three-fourths of their practice. Nine per cent say that individual treatment represents from a quarter to a half of their practice, and 18 per cent give up to 24 per cent of their practice to individual treatment. Not one respondent devotes all his time to group therapy, suggesting that it is regarded as one of several therapeutic tools rather than an exclusive procedure.

The median practitioner (21 per cent) has been engaged in the practice of group psychotherapy for from 5 to 7 years. Others have practiced group treatment for varying periods of time: 10–15 years (22 per cent), 3–4 years (11 per cent), 2–3 years (10 per cent),

4–5 years (8 per cent), 1 year (3 per cent), 15–20 years (3 per cent), over 20 years (3 per cent), and less than 1 year (1 per cent).

Training in Individual and Group Psychotherapy

A great proportion (86 per cent) of group psychotherapists report that they were trained in individual psychotherapy. Of these, three-fifths received training by formal course work, 28 per cent by practical work under supervision, and 8 per cent by control analysis. A psychoanalytic training institute was the place of training for 25 per cent and a psychiatry department the scene of training of 16 per cent of the group psychotherapists studied. Fourteen per cent were trained in a university graduate setting and 12 per cent via a psychiatric residency. The Veterans' Administration served as the source of training for 10 per cent, a social agency for 9 per cent, a school of social work for 5 per cent, and other training institutes for 4 per cent.

The majority (59 per cent) of group psychotherapists report that they are self-trained in group psychotherapy. Of the 41 per cent who report formal training, a department of psychiatry was the training site for 23 per cent, a graduate university department for 20 per cent, while psychoanalytic institutes and the Veterans' Administration each accounted for 17 per cent. The Postgraduate Center for Psychotherapy was the scene of training for 15 per cent, the National Psychological Association for Psychoanalysis for 6 per cent. Two per cent reported receiving formal training with S. R. Slavson or Alexander Wolf.

A number of different kinds of formal group training are reported. Of the training listed, 23 per cent consisted of introductory courses, 22 per cent of continuous case seminars, 21 per cent of courses in techniques, 18 per cent of workshops, and 15 per cent of instruction in theory. In each of these types of formal training the median amount of instruction consisted of only one course. The median length of the total workshop experience was 14 months, and the median continuous case seminar lasted for 17 months. The median introductory course took 10 months, the median technique course took 13 months, and the median theory course also took 13 months. The amount of time spent in these training procedures ranged from a few months to over 5 years.

Almost all (92 per cent) of those who have had training in group psychotherapy also report training in individual psychotherapy. Seventy-six per cent of respondents who have had no group training have had training in individual psychotherapy. Of those respondents who have had training in individual psychotherapy, 55 per cent have also had group training. Two-thirds of those not trained in individual psychotherapy are also not trained in group psychotherapy.

Experience of Therapists as Patients in Individual Treatment

Sixty-three per cent of practitioners have had experience as patients in individual psychoanalysis or psychotherapy. Of those with such experience, there were approximately 3 persons who had individual psychoanalysis for every person who had individual psychotherapy. The median respondent who had been analyzed reported 3 visits a week for 39 months of treatment. The median respondent who had received psychotherapy reported 2 sessions a week for 21 months.

Five per cent of the individual analyses and 3 per cent of the psychotherapy sessions had continued for over 7 years. The psychoanalyses not only tended to have more sessions per week, but also tended to take longer than psychotherapy. Two per cent of those receiving psychotherapy, however, reported 6 sessions a week, and 5 per cent reported 5 sessions a week; 16 per cent of those in psychoanalysis had 5 sessions a week and 27 per cent reported 4 sessions weekly.

Of those group psychotherapists who had received individual treatment, there was a tendency for practitioners in the East and especially in New York to have been in treatment for longer than practitioners in other parts of the country. Group psychotherapists in the South and Central parts of the country reported less individual treatment, with 46 per cent of Southern respondents and 45.5 per cent of Central respondents reporting no individual treatment, compared with a national average of 63 per cent.

The practitioners who have had formal training in group psychotherapy were patients in individual treatment for a longer period than those practitioners who have received no formal group psychotherapy training.

Experience of Therapists as Patients in Group Treatment

Approximately one-third of all respondents had been patients in a group. Of these, half experienced group psychotherapy and the other half were in an analytic group. The median analytic group met once a week for 15 months; the median psychotherapy group met once a week for 9 months. About half the respondents who had been patients in a group had been in treatment which combined individual and group experience. About a third also had alternate meetings in which the patients met without the psychotherapist.

Cities in the Midwest had the greatest proportion of group therapists who have not had experience as a patient in either group psychotherapy or group psychoanalysis. The relatively small proportion of urban Midwest respondents with such experience tended to have the least time in a group, averaging 3 months. Practitioners in the East and especially in New York City tended to have the longest experience as patients in groups, both psychotherapy and psychoanalytic. New York City respondents who had been in a group were somewhat more likely to have been in an analytic than a psychotherapy group. Respondents in the Los Angeles area who had been in a group were far more likely to have been in a psychotherapy than in an analytic group.

Although a number of respondents identified their individual therapeutic experiences as a "didactic" analysis or "training," no one identified his group experience as "didactic" or "training." The concept of a "didactic" or "training" group analysis does not seem to exist. Although some practitioners were in groups consisting of other psychotherapists, a number mentioned that these groups became "regular" therapeutic groups.

Supervision and Teaching

Supervision of others in the practice of group psychotherapy was reported by 47 per cent of the respondents. The median length of this supervisory experience was 28 months. Of those who have supervised, 20 per cent have done so for 7–12 months, 18 per cent for 19–24 months, 17 per cent for 25–36 months, 12 per cent for over 96 months, 11 per cent for 37–48 months, 7 per cent for 61–72 months, 6 per cent for 49–60 months, 4 per cent for less than 6 months, 2 per cent for 85–96 as well as 13–18 months, and 1 per cent for 73–84 months.

The median group under supervision received such supervision for a period of 11 months, or 35 hours. This median amount of supervision was reported regardless of how many of the therapists' groups had been supervised. The median therapist who had received supervision had had 1.2 groups supervised.

Over one-fourth of practitioners (29 per cent) had taught group psychotherapy. Of these instructors, 52 per cent taught general courses, 29 per cent taught techniques, and 19 per cent taught introductory courses. The instructors had given an average of one course in each of these areas.

Description of Therapy Groups

Although some practitioners report having as many as 20 therapy groups, the median group psychotherapist has only 1 group, whether his practice is private, institutional, or in any other context. There is no significant difference in the number of groups conducted by those in private practice as compared with those in institutional settings. Forty-seven per cent of all the groups reported are in private practice settings, 19 per cent are institutional inpatient, and 14 per cent are in a social agency. Eleven per cent are institutional outpatient, 4 per cent are in a school, 3 per cent are state hospital inpatient, 1 per cent are general hospital inpatient and 1 per cent are in general hospital outpatient treatment.

Fifty-three per cent of all groups include both men and women, 23 per cent are all male, 18 per cent are all female, and 2 per cent are family groups. Children, parents, married couples, and homogeneous disease groups each account for 1 per cent of the groups reported. Seventy-eight per cent of all groups are described as general adult. Of the remaining, 8 per cent are between 26 and 40 years of age and 6 per cent are adolescents. Age groups 5–11, 12–15, 16–18, and 19–25 each accounted for 2 per cent of the groups reported. The groups of patients over 40 and of children under the age of 5, together came to less than 1 per cent of the groups reported.

Size of Groups

The number of patients in the therapy groups reported exhibited a tremendous range. There were groups reported with 30, 40, 50, and 100 patients. There were also groups with 2 members. The most popular number of patients in a group was 8 (31 per cent). Among the number of patients reported in other groups were: 7 (17 per cent), 6 (16 per cent), 10 (9 per cent), 5 (7 per cent), 9 (6 per cent), 11–12 (5 per cent), 4 (4 per cent), 3 (2 per cent), and 13–14, 15–19, 20–29 (1 per cent each).

The setting of the therapy had some relationship to the size of the group. Groups in institutional settings tended to be relatively larger than groups in other settings. Thus, 10 people were more likely to occur in a general hospital outpatient group than in any other format. The only groups with more than 25 members were reported from inpatient situations. State hospital groups tended to be of median size, as did groups in social agencies. The smallest size groups tended to be in private practice, school, and Veterans' Administration situations.

The goal of the group had slight correlation with its size. Membership ranging from 3 to over 100 was reported in both psychotherapy and counseling groups. Psychoanalytic groups ranged from 3 to 25. Guidance and supportive groups tended to be the least extreme in size and to have a range of 5 to 15 patients.

Therapy Goals of Groups Reported

A number of different goals for groups were reported. Forty-eight per cent were described as psychotherapy groups, 28 per cent as psychoanalytic, 14 per cent as counseling, 2 per cent as guidance, and 1 per cent as supportive groups. A fraction of 1 per cent were described as psychodrama groups.

Although there were representatives of each discipline doing every kind of group psychotherapy, there was a tendency for psychiatrists to have more psychoanalytic and psychotherapy groups than psychologists or social workers. Fifty-three per cent of psychiatrists' groups are classified as psychotherapy groups, while 31 per cent are psychoanalytic and 7 per cent having counseling goals. Forty-nine per cent of psychologists' groups are for psychotherapy while 26 per cent are psychoanalytic and 12 per cent are counseling groups. Psychotherapy is the goal of 41 per cent of social workers' groups, while 17 per cent are psychoanalytic and 31 per cent are counseling groups. Psychologists and social workers are especially likely to have groups for supportive therapy, and psychiatrists are especially likely to have groups for guidance.

Session Length

The most popular (60 per cent) length of group sessions was 90 minutes. Sixty-minute sessions account for 20 per cent of the groups. Other session lengths reported include 75 minutes (7 per cent), 50 minutes (7 per cent), 120 minutes (4 per cent), 100 minutes (1 per cent), and over 120 minutes (1 per cent).

The goals of the group have some relationship to its typical session length. Fifty-six per cent of the psychotherapy groups met for 90 minutes, 22 per cent for 60 minutes, and 10 per cent for 50 minutes. Three-fourths of the psychoanalytic groups met for 90 minutes and 7 per cent met for 120 minutes. Fifty-one per cent of the counseling groups met for 90 minutes, 26 per cent for 60 minutes, and 13 per cent for 75 minutes. Exactly half the guidance groups met for 60 minutes. Sessions for groups receiving supportive therapy tended to be shorter than those for any other kind of psychotherapy group.

Frequency of Meeting

Eighty-one per cent of the groups reported meet once a week. Fifteen per cent meet twice a week. Group meetings 3 times a week, 4 or more times a week, once every other week, and once a month, each account for 1 per cent of groups reported. The great majority of groups (84 per cent) do not meet in alternate sessions, although 13 per cent do have one weekly alternate session. Two per cent have optional alternate meetings, and a fraction of one per cent of the groups have more than one alternate meeting a week.

Fees

In settings in which a fee is charged, the most frequent (39 per cent) single session fee is in the $7.50–$9.99 range. Other fee ranges reported are $5–$7.49 (31 per cent), $.50–$4.99 (20 per cent), $10–$14.99 (6 per cent), $15–$19.99 (2 per cent), and over $20 (2 per cent). The respondents were also asked to give the median fee per group, and their answers were slightly different from their statement of single session fee ranges. The most frequent (31 per cent) median fee per group is $7.50–$9.99. Other fees reported are $5–$7.49 (24 per cent), $10–$12.49 (16 per cent), $2.50–$4.99 (16 per cent), $.50–$2.49 (7 per cent), $12.50–$14.99 (3 per cent), $15–$19.99 (2 per cent), $20–$25 (1 per cent), and a fraction of a per cent charge over $30 median fee per group member.

There was some relationship between fee per session and location of practice. Communities in the Midwest and Southwest were the only ones reporting fees of over $25 per session. Fees on the West Coast were somewhat lower than those on the Eastern seaboard. The South and Central parts of the country have a slight tendency to charge lower fees than the East and West.

There is a consistent tendency for psychiatrists to charge more than psychologists and lesser tendency for psychologists to charge more than social workers. Thus, a median fee of over $9 per session is charged by 23 per cent of psychiatrists, 9 per cent of psychologists, and 8 per cent of social workers.

Any statement of fees must include the caution that different areas may have great differences in the cost of living, so that the same fee may have different purchasing power from one community to the other. Kubie, in commenting on incomes of psychoanalysts in the only comparable study published to date, observes that the difference in living costs between Baltimore and New York may make a $25,000 income in New York the purchasing equivalent of a $15,000 income in Baltimore[2]. The New York psychoanalyst with two or three children, suggests economist Eli Ginzberg, might have to spend much more than his Baltimore counterpart who lives comparably: $2,000 more for rent, $5,000 more for education, $1,000 more for recreation, $500 more for automobile upkeep, and $500–$1,000 more for domestic help. Differences between other parts of the country may be relevant.

Training for Group Psychotherapists

The field is so recent that many of the creators of modern group psychotherapy are still young and active. These pioneers began working in the area long before the availability of formal instruction. They trained others via preceptorships and other relatively informal procedures. It is not surprising, therefore, that there is a considerable proportion of group psychotherapists without much formal training. Now that the field is becoming more stabilized there is an opportunity to appraise the possible directions which preparation for group psychotherapy may take.

Although it is obvious that training for group counseling is likely to be different from training for psychoanalytic group psychotherapy, there is considerable agreement on what constitutes adequate training for doing group psychotherapy. There would be agreement that it is more difficult to do effective group psychotherapy than it is to do effective individual psychotherapy. Therefore, the group psychotherapist should be a fully qualified individual psychotherapist before he begins working with groups. One reason for this is that group treatment almost inevitably involves some activity in individual psychotherapy, since group psychotherapy is so widely used as an adjunct to individual treatment. Another reason is that groups consist of individuals and even though group and individual treatment differ, a knowledge of individual psychodynamics is essential in order to truly understand group psychodynamics.

The training in individual psychotherapy should include appropriate course work, as well as adequate supervision by a senior psychotherapist of several cases which the trainee is treating. Another requirement should be an experience as a patient in personal psychoanalysis or other psychotherapy. Such an experience is highly desirable, both in order to assist the psychotherapist to handle his own problems of living and also in calling attention to blind spots which might otherwise lead to counter-transference difficulties. A number of nationally accepted training programs in individual psychotherapy take four years of relatively fulltime work. It is difficult to see how anyone could become qualified to do individual psychotherapy in a period of less than three years.

Training for group psychotherapy should ideally begin *after* completion of training in individual treatment. It should begin with appropriate course work. A continuous case seminar has been found to be very useful. In such a seminar one or more groups are presented and discussed over an extended period. Another useful training format is the workshop. Trainees on the same level meet regularly with an experienced group psychotherapist to discuss problems which they have encountered in conducting group treatment.

Experience as an observer or recorder in a group conducted by an experienced group psychotherapist is especially desirable. This permits the trainee to learn in a realistic and yet relatively nonthreatening situation. A year as an observer or recorder is a probable minimum for this kind of experience to be most helpful. In a shorter period the trainee will not be likely to observe the stages in the life cycle of a group. After some time as an observer or recorder, the trainee will be able to profit from experience as a co-therapist in which he shares in the therapeutic leadership of the group.

Part of adequate training for the practice of group psychotherapy should be the experience as a patient in a psychotherapy group. Having been a patient in a group makes the trainee much more sensitized to how patients actually experience group psychotherapy. It will also help the trainee in problem areas that may not have been reached in his experience as a patient in individual treatment. Since so many group patients are also individual patients, his own group experience will help the trainee to appreciate the difference between individual and group psychotherapy.

Conducting groups under supervision for a minimum period of two years is an almost indispensable part of training for group psychotherapy. There is no substitute for experience, and this is perhaps even more true of group than of individual psychotherapy because group treatment is so much more complex and multifaceted. Supervision can help to insure that the experience will involve learning and growth rather than repetition of what may be undesirable procedures.

Organizations

A leading organization in the group psychotherapy field is the American Group Psychotherapy Association, which was started in 1943. Its headquarters are at 1790 Broadway in New York City. Qualified psychiatrists, psychologists, and social workers, are eligible to join. Its annual meetings usually occur in New York in January. For a few days prior to the annual meeting, a concentrated program is conducted for members in the form of institutes, conferences, and workshops. The AGPA has a number of regional societies. Anyone who is a member of AGPA is eligible to join the appropriate regional society. The regional societies to date include the following group psychotherapy societies: Delaware Valley, Eastern, Golden Gate, Louisiana, Maine, New Jersey, Northeastern, Southwestern, Tri-State Group (Ohio, Indiana, Kentucky), Baltimore-Washington, and Los Angeles.

Chronologically, the first organization of group psychotherapists was The American Society of Group Psychotherapy and Psychodrama, founded by J. L. Moreno. This organization meets annually, usually in New York and usually in March. Membership is open to qualified professionals. It is primarily concerned with the exploration of various facets of sociometry, psychodrama, and related techniques. The psychiatric, psychological, and social work professions are represented in this society in the proportions of 5:4:1.

Journals

The two leading journals in the field of group psychotherapy are each published quarterly. They are the *International Journal of Group Psychotherapy*, which is sponsored by the American Group Psychotherapy Association, and *Group Psychotherapy*, published by Beacon House in Beacon, New York. *Group Psychotherapy* was originally called *Sociatry* when it was started in 1947 by J. L. Moreno. It includes considerable material on sociometry and psychodrama as well as articles on various facets of group psychotherapy.

The *International Journal of Group Psychotherapy* was started in 1950 under the editorship of S. R. Slavson. It is primarily concerned with psychoanalytically oriented group treatment, although discussions of other kinds of group treatment also occur. It has a book review section which reports on new books in the field. The current editor is Harris B. Peck.

Most of the clinical journals in psychology, psychiatry, and psychotherapy now regularly carry articles on group psychotherapy. Social work journals also carry reports on social workers' use of group psychotherapeutic techniques.

Need for Research and Reporting Results

Group psychotherapists are continually confronting unusual and interesting psychotherapeutic situations in the course of their daily work. There should be a continuing flow of such experiences into the ongoing body of knowledge in the field of group psychotherapy. The field is so new that reports of clinical experience, though not research, may constitute very significant additions to what is known. It seems to us that we group psychotherapists have an obligation to contribute to knowledge in this field which has enabled us to help our patients so considerably. The field is so dynamic that each group psychotherapist should attempt to add his own experiences to the corpus of the group psychotherapeutic arsenal.

Few settings permit a group psychotherapist the luxury of conducting research as well as clinical service work. Formal research is based on the examination of hypotheses, and is, of course, likely to yield the most generalized kinds of findings. If circumstances or lack of funds make such formal research impossible, then less formal procedures may also be employed, with a recognition that so-called "clinical research" is not the kind of empirical research that meets operational criteria.

"Clinical research" is the name for observations made by a group therapist about what happened in a group that he or someone else conducted. It is not likely to qualify as research because it seldom pays heed to the minimal criteria for research. Such criteria would include a literature search in the corpus of both group dynamics and group psychotherapy in order to pinpoint how the particular problem was related to previous work. A formal statement of the hypotheses would also be present, along with an explicit and operational definition of the terms used.

If we employ any measuring devices, they should be made as explicit as possible. The group therapist has a wide array of procedures on which he can draw for measurement of changes in the individual: Q-sort, rating scales, semantic differential, projective tests, paper and pencil tests, and measures of anxiety and problem check lists[3-11]. If he is measuring a group phenomenon, it is all the more important to be as explicit as possible. If we say that the group climate changed, how do we establish the criteria for change? If we say that the group members expressed aggression at a session, can we describe the aggression in terms that are meaningful to others? If we are introducing a stimulus into the group, do we describe the stimulus clearly enough for others to replicate it if they wish to do so?

Another consideration is that of the control group. How can we know, without the use of a control group which is watched as closely as possible and compared with the group which is in the experimental situation, whether what happened in the experimental group was the result of chance or merely of the passage of time?

Such criteria are not difficult to consider, yet they can make the difference between an interesting piece of "clinical research" and a controlled experiment which may be a significant contribution to knowledge in the field.

There is a burning need for more research in group psychotherapy, and almost every setting can lend itself to a research application. Continued research re-examination of the "givens" of group psychotherapy and research scrutiny of new procedures will help to make group psychotherapy a more precise and more effective procedure. Such re-examination and scrutiny will make us ever more effective in our ability to help those who must be not only the starting point but also the conclusion of any consideration of group psychotherapy: patients in a group.

References

1. WINICK, C., KADIS, A. L., and KRASNER, J. D., Training and professional practice of American group psychotherapists. *Internat. J. Group Psychotherapy* 11:419, 1961.
2. KUBIE, L. S., A pilot study of psychoanalytic practice in the United States. *Psychiatry* 13:227, 1950.
3. LEVITT, E. E., *Clinical Research Design and Analysis in the Behavioral Sciences*. Springfield, Thomas, 1961.

4. HARE, A. P., *Handbook of Small Group Research.* New York. Free Press, 1962.

5. STEPHENSON, W., *The Study of Behavior: Q-Technique and Its Methodology.* Chicago, Univ. of Chicago Press, 1953.

6. BARRON, F., An ego strength scale which predicts response to psychotherapy. *J. of Consult. Psychol.* 17:327, 1953.

7. OSGOOD, C. E., SUCI, G. J., and TANNENBAUM, P. A., *The Measurement of Meaning.* Urbana, Univ. of Illinois Press, 1957.

8. BELL, J. E., *Projective Techniques.* New York, Longmans Green, 1948.

9. ANDERSON, H. H., and ANDERSON, G. S., eds., *An Introduction to Projective Techniques.* New York, Prentice Hall, 1951.

10. ABT, L. A., and BELLAK, L., eds., *Projective Psychology.* New York, Knopf, 1953.

11. WATSON, R. I., *The Clinical Method in Psychology.* New York, Harper, 1957.

appendixes

Appendix I. Two-Year Part-Time Training Program in Group Psychotherapy

FOR its possible adaptation by other facilities, listed below is the current curriculum of the Group Psychotherapy Department of the Postgraduate Center for Psychotherapy. This curriculum is the result of a program that began in 1951. It is designed to be taken over a two-year period and, including supervision, requires ten hours a week of the candidate. It includes courses, workshops, and clinical experience under supervision, as observer and therapist in a group setting, as well as personal group therapy. Each session or class listed below meets for one hour.

FIRST YEAR, FALL SEMESTER

Introduction to Group Psychotherapy Program   *8 sessions*
This course includes a discussion of the over-all plan of the group therapy program. The role of the candidate is delineated and preparation for taking over a therapy group is begun.

Workshop: Initial Phase of Group Psychotherapy   *8 sessions*
This workshop covers the following topics: treatment planning, selection of patients, group compositions, preparation for first group session, initial resistance phenomena to and in group therapy, multiple transference phenomena. Discussion of relevant literature is included.

181

Laboratory in Group Psychotherapy   *15 sessions*

Through participation, an interaction learning experience in group psychotherapy is provided. An experimental situation is set up to elicit and explore various interpersonal and group phenomena. The process is intended to provide a means of integration through personal experience with basic concepts in group psychotherapy. The course is research oriented.

Continuous Group Case Seminar   *15 sessions*

This course follows a group in treatment from its inception by means of a one-way screen. Sessions are immediately discussed and analyzed.

Clinical Workshop   *8 sessions*
(to alternate with Staff Conferences)

This workshop offers the participants an opportunity to present and discuss the variety of clinical problems with which they are confronted in their psychotherapy groups.

Personal Analytic Group Therapy

All trainees are expected to have started personal group analytic therapy when they begin treating patients in groups. The time and cost of treatment are arranged individually by the trainee with a group analyst whose qualifications have been determined in advance as acceptable. Not less than 80 sessions are required.

FIRST YEAR, SPRING SEMESTER

Workshop: Integration of Theory and Techniques I   *15 sessions*

This course explores the techniques involved in treating such difficult problems in group therapy as the borderline patient, the silent member, the monopolizer, the acting-out patient, the masochist, the sexually disturbed patient, and the psychosomatic patient. It includes an intensive study of the relevant literature.

Continuous Group Case Seminar   *15 sessions*

This course follows a group in treatment from its inception by means of a one-way screen. Sessions are discussed and analyzed immediately.

Clinical Workshop, *Continued*
(to alternate with Staff Conferences)

Personal Analytic Group Therapy, *Continued*

SECOND YEAR, FALL SEMESTER

Workshop: Integration of Theory and Techniques II   *15 sessions*

This course consists of an historial orientation and an exploration of the philosophical position of leading figures in the field of group psychotherapy. There is intensive study of the relevant literature.

Research Problems in Group Psychotherapy   *8 sessions*
(to alternate with Staff Conferences)

This course examines how research may be and has been applied to group psychotherapy. There is a systematic presentation of how a research problem is formulated, planned and executed, and how to implement research opportunities in private and institutional treatment situations. This course also develops research designs for the candidates' special projects.

Readings in Group Psychotherapy   *15 sessions*

This course consists of a review of the literature emphasizing the historical development of psychoanalytic group psychotherapy and an evaluation of the philosophy and theory of major issues as they relate to clinical practice.

Clinical Workshop, *Continued*   *15 sessions*
(to alternate with Staff Conferences)

Personal Analytic Group Therapy, *Continued*

SECOND YEAR, SPRING SEMESTER

Research Problems in Group Psychotherapy, *Continued*
(to alternate with Staff Conferences)

Readings in Group Psychotherapy   *15 sessions*

This course consists of an evaluation of the literature in its application to major issues in the field of group psychotherapy. In addition, specific group therapy approaches and techniques are appraised as they relate to the therapists' clinical practice.

Workshop: Special Constellations, Settings and Treatment Planning of Psychotherapy Groups   *15 sessions*

This course is devoted to a study of constellations, settings, and treatment planning for children, adolescents, parents, couples, older persons, and teachers.

Laboratory in Group Psychotherapy, *Continued*   *15 sessions*

Personal Analytic Group Therapy, *Continued*

Advanced Clinical Workshop   *15 sessions*

This seminar offers the advanced group psychotherapists an apportunity to share, discuss, and work through clinical problems in group psychotherapy.

Appendix II. Week-end Workshop in Group Psychotherapy

THERE is a growing interest in relatively brief but concentrated training experiences in group psychotherapy, for professionals whose schedule permits only a two-day week-end period away from their other commitments. Summarized below is the schedule of a recent week-end workshop. On the basis of their background and experience, the workshop members were assigned to either an intermediate or an advanced section. Each member chose one of the three workshops offered concurrently during the morning, afternoon, and evening sessions.

Friday, 9:00—10:00 A.M.
>   Introduction to Workshops
>   Assignment to Workshops

Morning Workshops

> 10:00 A.M.—12:30 A.M.—Friday and Saturday
> 9:00 A.M.—11:30 A.M.—Sunday

I Observation of a group by means of a one-way screen followed by discussion of the session.

II The analysis of oral dependence in group psychotherapy.

III Dealing with sexual problems in group therapy.

Afternoon Workshops

2:00 P.M.—4:00 P.M.—Friday and Saturday
12:30 P.M.—3:00 P.M.—Sunday

IV   Contributions of group dynamics to the practice of group psychotherapy.

V   Special problems of transference and counter-transference with character neuroses in group therapy.

VI   Acting out in group psychotherapy.

Evening Workshops

6:00 P.M.—8:00 P.M.—Friday and Saturday
7:15 P.M.—9:15 P.M.—Sunday

VII   Concurrent individual and group treatment.

VIII   Group therapy meetings without the analyst.

IX   Working through in individual and group analysis.

Panel Discussion

3:30 P.M.—5:00 P.M.—Sunday

Each workshop provides the panel with a statement of the central problems discussed by its members.

indexes

author index

Abrahams, J., 80, 100, 148
Abrams, A., 147
Abt, L., 162, 178
Ackerman, N. W., 23, 65
Altshuler, I. M., 85, 100
Ansbacher, H., 130, 131
Ansbacher, R., 130, 131
Anthony, E. J., 10, 23, 55, 65
Aronson, M., 100

Bach, G. S., 21, 23, 80, 99
Bailey, W. C., 147
Barron, F., 178
Bell, J. E., 178
Bellak, L., 162, 178
Benjamin, H., 32
Berger, M. M., 130
Berliner, A. K., 147
Betlheim, S., 130
Bieber, T. B., 109, 116
Bierer, J., 14, 18, 22, 27
Bion, W., 85, 100
Boles, G., 23
Bross, R. B., 116, 162
Brunner-Orne, M., 147, 148
Bry, T., 148
Burrow, T., 12, 22

Cameron, D. E., 18, 23
Cholden, L., 80, 99
Coleman, M. L., 37
Corsini, R. J., 148
Cortez, S., 31

De Schill, S., 65

Dreikurs, R., 80, 100
Durkin, H., 21, 23, 116, 148
Dworin, J., 32

Eliot, T. S., 84
Ewing, J. A., 148
Ezriel, H., 21, 23, 85, 100

Feiber, C., 148
Fine, L., 31
Flowerman, S., 116
Fort, J. P., 147
Foulkes, S. H., 1, 10, 14, 15, 23, 85, 100
Frank, J. D., 21, 23, 65, 85, 100
Freedman, M. B., 53, 65
Freud, S., 13, 85, 130
Furst, W., 65

Ginott, H., 65
Glatt, M. M., 18
Glatzer, H. T., 65, 116, 148
Greenbaum, H., 148
Greene, J. S., 116
Grotjahn, M., 162
Gutheil, E., 130

Hadden, S. B., 85, 100, 162
Hare, A. P., 177
Haskell, M., 147
Holt, H., 23, 48, 100, 130, 131, 148
Horney, K., 85, 100
Hulse, W. C., 60, 65, 85, 100, 116, 148
Huston, J., 31

Igersheimer, W. W., 148

189

subject index